The Trail of the Past

# WALKING WITH BOERHAAVE IN LEIDEN

CIP-DATA KONINKLIJKE BIBLIOTHEEK, DEN HAAG

Walking

Walking with Boerhaave in Leiden : the trail of the past /
[ed.: A.M. Luyendijk-Elshout ... et al. ; transl. from the
Dutch by E. Kegel-Brinkgreve]. – Leiden : Caecilia
Foundation. – Ill., maps
Transl. of: Wandelen met Boerhaave in en om Leiden. –
Leiden : Caecilia Stichting, 1994. – With ref.
ISBN 90-801423-2-8
Subject headings: Boerhaave, Herman / historic monuments ;
Leiden / walking trails ; Leiden.

## COLOPHON

ISBN nr. 90-801423-2-8
Published by the Caecilia Foundation, Lange St. Agnietenstraat 10,
2312 WC Leiden.
Editor: Dr. A.M. Luyendijk Elshout. Assistant-editor: Ms. M.J.C. Stokman.
Translated from the Dutch original by Dr. E. Kegel-Brinkgreve.
Lay-out: Studio Henk de Bruin, Leiden.
Printer: Groen, Leiden.
This publication has been made possible by a grant of the Wellcome
Foundation, London.

PREFACE

There are many Foundations and Societies in Leiden and its surroundings which at times join forces in their efforts to preserve the rich architectural heritage of the past. They are associated in the consultative body 'Cultureel Erfgoed Leiden'; and it was in this assembly that the idea was put forward by Mr. D.E. Krantz to publish a little book on the subject of Herman Boerhaave and the places in the town and its surroundings where this famous physician and scientist has lived and worked.

There was also an immediate cause for this initiative. At that time the Museum Boerhaave, National Museum of the History of Science and Medicine, was nearing its completion; and this is housed in the restored building of the former St. Caecilia Hospital, where Boerhaave was wont to give his clinical lectures.

Boerhaave has close links with the town and its University. There is even something paradoxical in the contrast between his international fame – which greatly added to the renown of the Leiden University – and the prosaic fact that he hardly ever left the town where he lived. 'Town and Gown', the ties between the town and its University, are pre-eminently symbolised in the figure of Herman Boerhaave.

These links are also evident in the fact that inhabitants of the town as well as the University have sponsored this publication. The authors of the several contributions also belong to these two spheres. We owe much to their expert knowledge, and to the time and energy they have been willing to expend on the research and writing of these essays.

The final editing was entrusted to Professor A.M. Luyendijk-Elshout M.D.; the English translation has been made by Dr. E. Kegel-Brinkgreve.

The Friends of the Museum Boerhaave, who are joined in the Caecilia Foundation, have been closely involved in the project; hence it has been decided to publish the book under the auspices of this Foundation.

Leiden. March 1994      Prof. Dr. A. Rörsch I.C.E,
President of the Caecilia Foundation.

9

# 1. INTRODUCTION

**H**erman Boerhaave, *Communis Europae Praeceptor*, 'Teacher of all Europe', has played an important role in the cultural history of the West. That is not only due to his fame as a physician, but above all to his ideas about the life processes in nature. His iatro-mechanical views had a liberating influence on physicians and natural scientists, who still had to struggle against an allegorical way of conceptualising 'mysterious' forces supposedly to be found in nature. Boerhaave has mobilised all his energy against such concepts in the field of science, appealing to the mechanical laws which could be applied to the natural life processes in health and sickness. By means of this approach he has constructed a medical system which could serve as the starting-point for the development of physiology and pathology. His contributions to the sciences of chemistry and botany should be viewed in the same light.

Although Boerhaave's theories on the diagnosis and therapy of diseases continued to find adherents up to the second half of the nineteenth century, in the cultural history of the West his repute is mainly due to the simplicity and clarity of his system, on which the tuition of medical students was founded.

By his successors Boerhaave has often been labelled as an eclectic: a scientist who collects data from extant knowledge for a new system. It is true that his dislike of allegorical conceptualising has made him keep wholly aloof from speculative theories with regard to physiology, which yet eventually would be capable of creating the prospect of a new field of experimental research. Later generations who focused on the role of Boerhaave in the development of medicine have often criticised him for not having discovered 'anything new'. The work of G.A. Lindeboom M.D., the pre-eminent Dutch authority on Boerhaave, has shown that this view does not provide adequate grounds for depreciating Boerhaave's fame. The mutual relations of scholars in Europe towards the end of the seventeenth century, and in particular the enthusiasm about the theory of Isaac Newton, have triggered off a cultural movement which has been valued at its true worth by later physicians and historians as well; and it cannot be doubted that in this cultural movement Herman Boerhaave has played a key role.

Boerhaave was born on December 31 1668 in Voorhout, the son of the minister Jacobus Boerhaave and his wife, Hagar Daelder. When he

11

was fourteen years old, his father sent him to the Grammar school in Leiden. He lodged in a house in the Breestraat, where his father tended to stay when his business in Leiden required this.

In 1684 he was enrolled at the University of Leiden as a student of theology and philosophy. In 1690 he graduated in philosophy, but his study of theology was interrupted by his interest in the study of medicine. During his student years in Leiden he lived with his stepmother Eva Dubois and the large family left behind by his father (who had died in 1683) in the 'Faliede Begijnhof' (Court of the Veiled Beguines). The former church of the 'Faliede Begijnen' housed both the University Library and the Anatomical Theatre. Moreover, by merely crossing the bridge over the Rapenburg, he was in the premises of the University, the Botanical Garden, or the Physical Theatre, where his teacher Burchard de Volder gave demonstrations of scientific experiments in physics.

In 1693 Boerhaave departed for Harderwijk, in order to graduate in medicine at that University. He was not to finish his theological studies, however. During a journey in the towing-barge he happened to become involved in a discussion of the theses of Spinoza, which had been condemned by the ecclesiastical authorities. He was blamed for this; hence his chances of an incumbency were lost and he had to give up his plans for a career as the healer of both spirit and body. He established himself in Leiden as a physician and continued to live in the house of his stepmother. He pursued his studies, gave private lessons in mathematics, and made a thorough study of chemistry.

In 1701 Boerhaave was nominated University lecturer in medicine, on the recommendation of Johan van den Bergh, at that time Secretary to the Board of Governors of the University. His inaugural lecture was well received, and at the very outset it was evident that the University of Leiden had enlisted a promising scientist. He taught the principles of medicine, physiology, and general pathology in a clear and systematic way.

In 1703 he was given the opportunity to hold an oration in which he could expound his views on health and sickness, which in the meantime had matured. In this argument he introduced in a masterly way his concept of disease, which was based on the science of mechanics.

The first little manual he wrote, the *Institutiones Medicae* (Medical Principles) which he published in 1708 for the benefit of the students, soon had to be reprinted. A year afterwards a work was published which focused rather on the clinical perspective, the *Aphorisms*, a title deriving from Hippocrates.

12

Boerhaave was appointed to his first Chair, in botany, in 1709. In his inaugural lecture he introduced for the first time his motto, which was to become famous: *Simplex veri sigillum*, 'Simplicity is the hallmark of truth'. Now he also became the managing director of the University's Botanical Garden, and as such he was entitled to live in the official residence in the Nonnensteeg.

In 1710 he married Maria Drolenvaux, daughter of a well-to-do merchant. She was to bear him a daughter, Johanna Maria, in 1712.

In his teaching of botany Boerhaave soon made his mark as well. Already in 1710 he edited an inventory of the plants to be found in the Botanical Garden, and he exerted himself to acquire exotic plants for the Garden via his extensive network of foreign correspondents. In 1714 Boerhaave was given the task to revive the clinical teaching in the Caecilia Gasthuis, which had been somewhat neglected by his colleagues. And when, moreover, he was in 1718 appointed to the Chair of Chemistry as well, it was Boerhaave who actually dominated the entire teaching of medicine and, with that, the image of the medical faculty in the University of Leiden. The lectures in anatomy were the only exception to this; they were entrusted to Bernhard Siegfried Albinus, a gifted and still young scientist, who had been recalled by Boerhaave from Paris where he was finishing his studies. Boerhaave was intimately acquainted with the Albinus family. He did not only concern himself with the careers of the boys among the eleven children, but he also held the funeral oration on the father of this numerous family, Bernhard Albinus. This former court physician to the King of Prussia had been appointed as Professor of Medicine in Leiden in 1702.

Already in 1724 Boerhaave had bought the country house Oud-Poelgeest. Here he found the peace and quiet which he needed in his busy life. Here he could also cultivate his social contacts, entertaining colleagues and foreign guests; here he organised musical evenings, and he also laid out an Arboretum. Many plants for which there was no room in the Botanical Garden found accommodation in the garden of Oud-Poelgeest. For the time being, however, Boerhaave, as the managing director of the Botanical Garden, was obliged to keep on the house in the Nonnensteeg; but in 1729, when he resigned from his professorships in botany and chemistry, he was free to acquire another house, also close to his work. In 1730 he bought Rapenburg 31, the house where in the past his illustrious predecessor, Franciscus de le Boë, Sylvius had lived. In this house he was to die on September 23, 1738.

HERMANNUS BOERHAAVE
Medicinæ, Botanices, Chemiæ
& Collegii practici, in ACAD. LUGD. BAT.
PROFESSOR ORDINARIUS.

1.    Herman Boerhaave. Copperplate by J. Houbraken from a drawing of J.
      Wandelaar (no date).

Boerhaave was an excellent and dedicated teacher. At the peak of his career, when he held three chairs, he gave five hours of lectures a day, during four days of the week. His average audience numbered eighty to hundred students, half of which were foreigners. They came from all Europe and after 1720 from the New World as well. During his professorate close to two thousand students were enrolled in the Medical Faculty.

One student of Boerhaave who was to become famous was the Swiss Albrecht von Haller, who graduated in Leiden in 1727, and who was to develop a wholly new school in physiology. The honorary title 'Teacher of all Europe' has been coined by him. And then we have the Swede Carolus Linnaeus, who became the founding father of the taxonomy of plants. Three generations of the famous Munro family came from Scotland to Leiden for their studies: John Munro in 1692, Alexander Munro in 1718, and the son of the latter, Alexander II, in 1747. In 1726 the Medical School in Edinburgh was set up in line with the Leiden model. For a full century the medical faculty of Vienna was also strictly to maintain the study programme as set up by Boerhaave. That was due to Gerard van Swieten, one of Boerhaave's most devoted students, who in 1745 had been called to Vienna by the young Empress of Austria, Maria Theresia. The numerous German and English students also contributed to the propagation of the Boerhavian doctrine, both in Berlin and London.

Boerhaave had many contacts with scientists within Europe as well as outside it. His correspondence, in particular the letters concerning the field of botany, bear witness to a widespread network of connections. He also gave consultations in writing to patients and colleagues abroad. He recommended, moreover, students for posts in foreign countries: Nicolas Bidloo for instance, who organised a hospital and gave clinical lectures in Moscow. Boerhaave's two nephews, Abraham Kaau Boerhaave and his brother Herman, also obtained good posts in Russia, which was swiftly developing in that period.

In 1728 Boerhaave was nominated as a member of the Académie Royale des Sciences in Paris, mainly because of his merits in the fields of botany and physics in general. In 1730 he became a corresponding member of the Royal Society in London. Boerhaave has never ventured beyond the boundaries of the Netherlands; but his name and work have become famous throughout the world.

A.M.L.-E

15

# 2. BOERHAAVE'S BIRTHPLACE IN VOORHOUT

In 1593 a Reformed congregation was founded in the ancient Foranholte, now Voorhout. To begin with, the clergyman of this parish also officiated in Noordwijkerhout; afterwards it was Kage (De Kaag) which was part of his cure. In 1662 the Reverend Jacobus Boerhaave was called as minister to this parish. He moved into a house which is still standing, and which must have been built in the second quarter of the seventeenth century. In this house his son Hermannus Boerhaave was born on December 31, 1668; this is why it is called 'Boerhaave's House'. An inscription above the front door reads *Porta patet tibi, sed magis cor* (The door is open to you, but our heart even more so). Herman was baptised on New Year's Day 1669, as is shown by the parish register of the Reformed Church in Voorhout.

Boerhaave's House is a 17th-century country house, built in approximately a hundred square meters of woodland. It is mainly on cultural-historical grounds that it deserves attention: its architectural merits are not outstanding, even if the pattern of some sections of the

2.    The Boerhaave House in Voorhout. Engraving by Anna C. Brouwer (1799).

3. Entry in the baptismal register of the Reformed Church in Voorhout (1667).

front is very rare in the cities of Western Holland. When one compares its present situation with a map, which has been drawn in February 1669 by the land surveyor Johan Douwe de Jong, it appears that during more than three centuries the immediate environment of Boerhaave's House has suffered only a few changes. When one enters the house, one becomes immediately aware of the atmosphere and the spacious design of an abode which in the seventeenth century was thought to be suitable for a distinguished citizen: a roomy hallway, paved with marble, a large and deep cellar, several living- and sleeping-rooms, a study, vast attics, and a very large kitchen, where one can still discern the place where formerly an enormous oven must have stood. An iron hearth plate under one of the mantel-pieces dates from the seventeenth century. In the largest living-room one still sees the recess for the box-bed in which Herman Boerhaave was born.

Important restorations of the building were recurrently effected – in the years 1768, 1908 and 1960. A very extensive restoration and renovation was completed in 1985. At the turn of the century the house was so much dilapidated that it must have been considered to be almost unfit for habitation. The wall on the side of the village had a large bulge, the rear side was cracked and sloped inwards. Several walls on the front side were out of plumb. Most of the brickwork was in need of pointing. The two main roofs of the central building drained into a gutter which ran across the attic; when it was winter

18

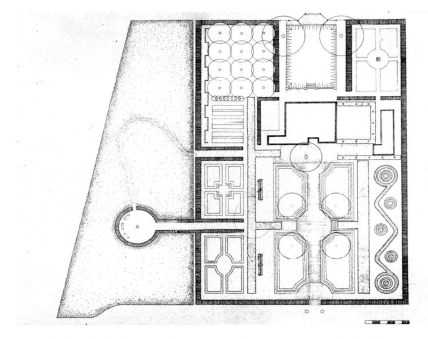

4.  Plan for the historical garden around the Boerhaave House. By the firm
    of Architects Bosch and Slabbers (1991).

and the openings at its ends were clogged up with ice or snow, the
water washed over the attic floor (in many places broken through and
patched up), which had, then, all the appearances of an inundated
field. Window frames had decayed, window panes of all sizes and
types had been inserted. This desolate situation was due to the
financial problems of the small Reformed congregation, which was
also burdened with the expensive upkeep of the little medieval
church. People were fully aware of the fact that Boerhaave's House
ought to be preserved; but it was very difficult to raise the necessary
funds. However, the matter began to make headway when the Reverend B. ter Haar Romeney took up office in Voorhout on September
1, 1907. He was certainly much interested in the preservation of this
cultural-historical monument; but it cannot be doubted that the Rev.
Ter Haar was also spurred on by the fact that the house, assigned to
him as his vicarage, was rather too draughty to be comfortable. He
managed to raise sufficient money to venture upon an extensive
restoration. This was carried out by the building contractor Jan

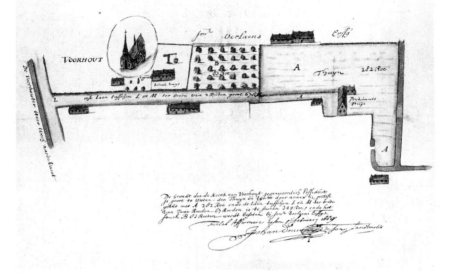

5.  The Boerhaave House. Drawing by the land surveyor J. Douwe de Jong, made one month after the birth of Herman Boerhaave.

Zuilhof, under the direction of two architects, Bremer and Slothouwer (who in this same period also participated in the building of the Peace Palace in The Hague). The double-ridged roof was replaced by a single large square roof, by means of which a large attic was created as well. A new kitchen was built on, and everything was done to restore the former solid structure.

Notwithstanding another restoration in 1960, it became evident in the early 1980s that drastic and expensive measures were again unavoidable if the house was to be preserved. Hence a number of inhabitants of Voorhout took the initiative to create the autonomous Foundation 'Boerhaave's House', of which the main objective was to raise funds for ensuring that the house would be preserved for many years to come. The Foundation had an auspicious start: already in 1983 repairing the house became a real option, and in 1985 the restoration and renovation were accomplished under the direction of the firm of architects J. Splinter in Leiden. The ancient beauty of the

6.    Rear view of the Boerhaave House (1990).

building's exterior has been restored, whereas the interior has been adapted to the requirements of our present time.

Boerhaave's House is situated in a beauty spot of close to one hundred square meters. Inhabitants are wont to call it the 'green heart of Voorhout'. In the 17th century the house was built in what was at that time the rural environment of Voorhout; it was meant to be a country seat, a house surrounded by a park of the kind which is nowadays characterised as a wooded garden. It seems, moreover, that it was also in the 17th century that it became the fashion in Europe to plant  carriage-drives of country houses with lime-trees; traces of this are still present in the old lime-trees which stand at the beginning of the path leading up to Boerhaave's House. The large wooded garden breathes an atmosphere of untroubled calm which gives the visitor a feeling of well-being. Lime-trees have some characteristics which are at times felt to be objectionable: suckers are apt to spring up around their main trunk, and on that trunk there may also appear large irregular knots; this becomes even more noticeable

7.    Front of the Boerhaave House (1990)

when the trees are pruned. Both characteristics, however, can be of use in a so-called *berceau* – the French term, originally meaning 'cradle', – which came to be used for arbours and covered walks, which became the fashion in 18th-century landscape gardening. Through the suckers springing up the *berceau* becomes more dense and continually rejuvenates itself; and the knots, which become more pronounced because the trees are pruned each year, give a very distinctive look to them. One of the valuable features of the garden of Boerhaave's House is an avenue of lime-trees which is by now more than a hundred years old, and which may well be unique in the whole of Europe. Covered walks planted with pears or other kinds of trees are known, but up to now the avenue with lime-trees of Boerhaave's House seems to be the only specimen. In spring and summer the rich foliage forms a green and cool tunnel, which impresses the visitor by its silent splendour; in wintertime the bare and knotty skeletons of the trees have a striking and eerie beauty.

The design of the garden displays the characteristics of the Renaissance style of gardening: a geometrical pattern, symmetrically structured by means of flower beds and axes. The formative elements of the garden are characteristic of this style: the *berceau*, the carriageway, trees symmetrically planted, a coppice, and a herb garden. The latter has been laid out in the past to honour Boerhaave, in the style of the Botanical Garden of the University of Leiden, of which he was at one time the director. In the back of the garden stands a solitary beech-tree, which is so old that it may well date from Boerhaave's time.

The garden is divided into strips, which originally were meant to serve ornamental as well as useful purposes (orchard, kitchen garden, and coppice). We intend to take the characteristics of the garden as our starting-point for further development: to preserve and, wherever possible, to strengthen them. In this we have the assistance of the Foundation for the Preservation of Nature and Landscape in South Holland. The herb garden is tended free of charge by voluntary workers, who for many years have been under the direction of Mrs. Waterreus-Knoppert.

Yet, notwithstanding all such efforts, the appearance of Boerhaave's garden is no longer in harmony with the house, which has been so beautifully restored in 1985. The garden has become very vulnerable, and the overall symmetrical pattern of the original has partially disappeared. That is why the Foundation 'Boerhaave's House' has taken the initiative for drawing up a new design for a garden in the classical style with the characteristics of the Dutch Renaissance – while preserving, naturally, the historical elements which are still present. The Foundation has commissioned the firm of Bosch and Slabbers B. Sc. (Landscape architects who specialise in historical gardens) to draw up a plan. That plan has turned out to be very attractive and is accepted by all parties concerned. The design will make it possible to add an aspect of crucial importance to the setting of Boerhaave's House. Almost no perfect specimens of historical gardens surrounding small country houses have survived in our country. If the plan is realised, as it has been drawn up, a bit of history will again be revived. It depends on the raising of the necessary funds whether this will turn out to be feasible; the realisation will be costly. And even then it will be several years before the garden is fully grown, so as to achieve the beautiful effect aimed at.

The garden turned out to be important in yet another way, namely as a site of historical finds. Coins, bowls of clay pipes, shoe buckles, and other objects emerged when the earth was worked. This alerted amateur treasure-seekers. And when excavations on the inside of the north-east front of the building laid bare the old cesspit, a careful search was set going for shards and fragments of earthenware, glass, and china. Two enthusiast investigators, Messrs. Kerkvliet and De Vries, patiently analysed and restored the finds; and so from the heap of nondescript shards and fragments a collection of ceramics came into being of more than 60 beakers, dishes, jugs, firepans, pipes, goblets, and other glassware, dating from the eighteenth century. Some Chinese porcelain was also present, which is possibly still older.

Now the collection shows up well in a beautiful showcase, which is in keeping with the style of the interior of the house, so carefully restored. And so the historical value of Herman Boerhaave's birthplace has acquired an additional dimension.                    J.Z.

# 3. PUPIL OF THE LATIN SCHOOL

In 1682 the father of the young Boerhaave took his son to Leiden, in order to enrol him as a pupil at the Latin School which, like the Grammar School of later times, prepared its pupils for University studies.

It is not known when this school was founded. It is certain, however, that it was already in existence in 1324: for at that time it is recorded that Count William III appointed its headmaster, Mr. Andries, as the secretary of his daughter Margaretha, who in this year was married to Louis of Bavaria. In that period the school had an accommodation between the House of Lockhorst, an old inn, and the Gravensteen. In 1431, however, a new building was erected on its present location, at the corner of the Lokhorststraat and the School-steeg. In 1597 this building was in a woeful condition; moreover, the authorities had banned further constructions of thatched roofs; hence the Town Council decided to erect a wholly new building on the same spot. This was done in 1599-1600, by the personnel of the town itself. The town mason Claes Cornelisz. van Es (who also played an important role in designing the new front of the town hall) probably was the master-builder. Other collaborators were the bricklayer and joiner in the town's employment, Jacob Dircxz den Dubbelden and Joris Andriesz.

The great assembly hall of the school was situated in the large attic. In 1651 the building, which had six classrooms, was enlarged by a seventh one, in view of the large number of pupils in the highest form. This enlargement was realised under the direction of the town architect, Arent van 's Gravensande. After that, up to the arrival of Herman, no further changes were made in the building. All windows still had the original frames, which only in 1830 and 1835 were replaced by the sash windows which are still there. In 1846 the school was again enlarged: the hallway was extended and the number of classrooms now came to ten, because the extension of 1651 (which in 1828 had been allotted to an office for gauging weights and measures) was again incorporated in the school. Moreover, another story and a new roof were added to the building. The town architect, Salomon van der Paauw was in charge of this renovation. Around 1900 the entire back part of the building was incorporated in the school, so that the number of classrooms came up to 12.

The school changed hands several times during the 19th and 20th century. In 1838 the Latin School was transformed into a gymnasium, a type of grammar school in which Latin and Greek had still a central place, but where modern languages and sciences were beginning to be taught as well. This was moved to a new building in the Doezastraat in 1883. A society called *Mathesis Scientiarum Genetrix* (Mathematics is the Mother of Science) during a large part of this period organised courses of technology, at first in evening classes and afterwards as a day school, in the ancient building, and a variety of other kinds of schools also found a temporary abode in it.

Eventually the Foundation Diogenes Leiden bought the building from the town. In 1980 this Foundation commissioned the architect J. Walraad from Brielle and the firm of contractors Du Prie in Leiden to institute an overall restoration. In the course of this restoration, which was effected in 1982, the attic was again put into use, the dormer windows were built, a connection was made between the new roof of the end house and that of the school; the great staircase, made in 1865 by the town architect Schaap, was extended from the first floor to the attic; some changes were made at a few of the windows. From 1982 onwards the building accommodated the Regional Schools Advisory Service. As far as we know, the Grammar School in Leiden is the only one in the Netherlands which from the time when the school was built, in 1599-1600, up to September 1988, that is, for almost 390 years, has uninterruptedly been serving purposes of education. From September 1988 onwards the school is being let to the publishing firm Compres.

Only the windows on the ground- and first floor of the beautiful frontage have been somewhat altered; the entrance section is just as it was built in 1650. The inscription above the little gateway reads in English: 'The Senate and People of Leiden have attended to the renovation, in the interest of piety, languages and the liberal arts, in the year 1600' (PIETATE LINGUIS ET ARTIBUS LIBERALIBUS S. P. Q. LUGDUNENSIS : RESTAU: C. ANo MDC )

Not only the school was built in 1600, but at the same time a house was put up for the headmaster. This building covered a part of what is at present the back-yard giving onto the Pieterskerkgracht, but extended still further up to the building-line of that street. One entered it through a beautiful little gateway, crowned with a[n image of] Pallas Athene and the motto *Tuta sub aegide Pallas* (Pallas is safe under her shield); she is flanked by two lions holding the town's arms. This so-called Headmaster's Gate was built in 1613, that is,

8. The Latin School. Coloured drawing by J.J. Bijlaert (ca. 1770).

somewhat later than the school, by the town mason at that time, Willem Claesz van Es. When the house was demolished in 1846, it left the town and was stored in the Rijksmuseum of Amsterdam; but when the Gravensteen was restored, the gate was brought back to Leiden, where it has now become part of the present entrance of the Gravensteen from the Gerecht. The headmaster's house was large because frequently students and pupils boarded with him – which undoubtedly yielded a welcome addition to his income. Nothing is known about the use of the classrooms, which one was allotted each form; the only thing we do know is that in Herman's time the large assembly room was in the attic.

By and large the curriculum in the grammar school was based on the medieval *trivium*, to which afterwards the *quadrivium* was added. The *trivium* consisted of grammar, dialectic, and rhetoric – hence the name of the 'Great or Trivial School' – which was only about 1670 changed into 'Latin School'.

The government and the supreme control of the school were vested in the Board of 'scholarchs', nowadays called Governors. This Board also presented the prizes: silver medals for the neatest exercise book, and books for the 'industry and virtue' of the pupil in question. Afterwards a pupil who had won the first prize also received a beautiful certificate. The headmaster taught the first form, and supervised the school generally; the deputy headmaster taught the second form. (When compared to the numeration used at present, the forms were numbered the other way round: the first form would now be the sixth, and so on.)

With regard to the curriculum from 1627 onwards we have been provided with detailed information by the historian Knappert. For in that year Leiden adopted the 'School order, made and decreed by the Lords of the States of Holland and West-Friesland for the Latin schools in this country, October 1, 1625', and this is the source of the description given by Knappert. In this 'ordre' a detailed programme is given, including the authors to be read in connection with that; it was laid down after the States had consulted the Rector and the Senate of the University, the headmasters of the majority of the grammar schools, and the delegates of the Synods of North and South Holland – the latter had to be consulted because, naturally, religious teaching was an important item in the curriculum. Henceforth the headmasters were bound to keep to these rules and regulations; moreover, all other forms of teaching, as well as books not included in the instruction, were banned. The aim of the States was to create a

28

uniform preparatory training for the University – that was, after all, the task of the grammar schools – with the attendant advantage that if need be, pupils could change from one school to another without any difficulty. Courts of justice, bailiffs, and officers were to supervise the compliance with these rules and regulations. It was a drastic intervention in the field of education, where in that period chaos prevailed.

The lessons in school began at 8, 9, and 10 o'clock in the morning, and 1, 2, and 4 o'clock in the afternoon. On Wednesday and Saturday they began at 7, 9, and 10 o'clock, in the afternoon at 1 o'clock. In that final hour the pupils were required to dispute in Latin; their performance determined their rank in the form's hierarchy.

How was the education organised? On Sunday the pupils who belonged to the Reformed Church were obliged to attend the morning- and afternoon services, under the supervision of their *praeceptores* (teachers); afterwards they must recount those points of the sermon which they managed to remember; when they were not successful in this, they were fined. The lessons began and ended each day with prayers, while in the morning a chapter of both the Old and the New Testament was read. In the higher forms the Psalms of David were sung, in the version of Datheen. Furthermore each class had its special religious programme.

In the sixth form the boys – there was no admittance for girls in the grammar schools – began by mastering Latin grammar from a book of Lud. Lithocomus, which had been published by Plantijn in Leiden in 1584; this was so highly esteemed, that it was several times reprinted, up to 1710, in a revised version made by Vossius. Moreover they read, among other things, the *Colloquia Familiaria* of Erasmus. One hour each day was devoted to a writing lesson. Wednesday and Saturday were reserved for again going over the subject-matter taught so far, and for religious instruction. In the fifth form Lithocomus was still in use, with the focus on syntax and other aspects of grammar. A beginning was made with writing Greek. Letters of Cicero were read, and the *Disticha de moribus ad filium*, 'Distichs on Morals, addressed to my son' were studied. This was a famous collection of moral maxims of Dionysius Cato: a schoolbook which up to the beginning of the 18th century was considered an exceptionally suitable means to teach the rudiments of grammar, poetry, and morals. The pupils, moreover, became acquainted with a little book of Erasmus, *De civilitate morum puerilium libellus*, (On civilised manners of the young). Wednesday and Saturday were again reserved here for again going over the subject matter, and also for catechism lessons and stylistic exercises.

In the fourth form the pupils engaged in translating four rather difficult Latin authors, whereas Greek was learnt during the afternoon, with the help of the *Grammatica Graeca* of Nicolas Clenardus (Cleynaerts, 1495-1542). Much attention was given to versification, in particular the metrics of the hexameter, a metre of Greek origin. Themes must be sought in pre-eminent Latin authors.

In the third form pupils continued with Clenardus' grammar, and read Aesop's beast fables. They were trained in speaking extempore, while trying to utilise their reading of Latin authors. There were also exercises in learning by heart; during the lessons in writing Latin prose the focus was on the epistolary style. During the hours of religious instruction the rhymed commentary on David's psalms was studied, a work of the famous Scotsman Buchanan.

In the second form the principles of rhetoric and logic were taught and used in the analysis of the orations of the famous author and orator Cicero. Moreover, a large amount of Greek was now read, with a rather more detailed Greek grammar, the *Syntaxis Graeca* of Joh. Possel (Rostock 1561). During the hours of religious teaching the Gospel of St. Luke and the Acts of the Apostles were read in Greek, and the main chapters of the Heidelberg catechism were commented upon. By now translations were made, not only from the Latin, but also of Dutch into Latin. This was the only hour in which explicit attention was given to Dutch. No other 'modern' languages were taught: naturally, because the future scholars and scientists were expected to use Latin, *the* international language!

The first form was divided into two parts. In the first one there was even more emphasis on logic; by now the more difficult Latin authors were also read. In Greek the pupils read Homer and Euripides. In this final year some hours were kept free for work at home; it is not clear whether in this time the pupils were meant to do their homework, or whether they were free to choose a subject to work upon. The curriculum of the second half of the first form comprehended for the first time subjects other than Latin, Greek, and logic, namely physics, mathematics, cosmography, geography, as well as general and Roman history. Wednesdays and Saturdays by now were also used for writing Latin verse, from 'funeral to hymeneal poems'. The subjects for stylistic exercises could now also be taken from sacred literature. During the lessons in religion heresies were reviewed and, of course, thoroughly refuted. For ecclesiastical history the *Sacra Historia*, 'Sacred History', written by Jog. Sleidanus, was used, in the edition published in 1626 by Elsevier in Leiden.

Finally, the boys were obliged to speak Latin to each other, both in and outside the school; their teachers must train them in 'civilised manners'. Moreover, the pupils were made to supervise one another, whether they had conversed in Dutch or bad Latin, or had displayed objectionable or coarse manners. Such occurrences should be noted down and submitted to the form's teacher. It appears from a document entitled *Some points*, which was meant to be used by the 'scholarchs' when 'the new headmaster' was to be appointed and which was written after 1663, that the pupils had yet another task: they were obliged to check the written work of one another and to point out mistakes. If their criticism was justified, they were entitled to the rank in the form's hierarchy, occupied by the pupil who had been so corrected. The latter was obliged himself to rectify his mistakes and to show his work to the teacher so that it was certain that the errors were set to rights. The headmaster was obliged to 'check each eight, or at the most fourteen days, whether the pupils perform their duty with regard to writing exercises, and whether they have a copy of the 'writing-master' and follow that model'.

When one surveys the curriculum, it must be granted that the pupils had to work very hard in those three years. Three years: for in each year they passed through two grades: the first lasting from July 1 to January 1, the second from January to July, with a steeply rising level of difficulty. Apart from the languages they acquired a smattering of logic and rhetoric; some moral principles were also imparted. A simple grammar constituted the beginning, and eventually the pupils were able to write Latin poetry and to dispute in that language. The curriculum was in the humanistic tradition, albeit under a severely religious, almost 'fundamentalist' watch and ward.

There may have been a few changes in this curriculum, but on the whole the account given above must be considered a fair description of the course of education followed by Herman Boerhaave in the grammar school. So much is certain, that it will not have become less demanding.

As has been said already, the Rev. Boerhaave went with Herman to Leiden in the summer of 1682, in order to enrol him as a pupil in the school. One reason for this decision must have been that Herman had a swelling on his left thigh, which did not heal. The expenses of treatment at home mounted up considerably, and Herman's father thought that in Leiden he could be treated better and cheaper. The

9.    The Latin School. Photograph by P.H. de Block van Scheltinga (1982).

headmaster examined Herman and concluded that he would easily be able to follow the programme of the third grade. This was due to the exceptionally good tuition which had been imparted to him at home by his father.

32

On Friday, July 19, Herman was registered at the University, as being 14 years old, 'living with his father on the Breestraat', and a pupil of the third form of the grammar school. Generally speaking, the pupils of that school were registered at the University when they had reached the fourth grade. This had to do with the fact that this registration entailed freedom of the excise duty on beer etc. and, moreover, that the person so registered came under the jurisdiction of the University instead of the town, and the former was more accommodating than the civil authorities!

The address given is worth noting. The Rev. Boerhaave did not himself possess a house in the Breestraat. He lived in the vicarage of Voorhout. It has been assumed in the past that Herman has boarded with Coenraad Uylhoorn, an instrument maker, as a day pupil of the school. Yet Uylhoorn has never lived in the Breestraat. Mr. Downer, former archivist of the city of Leiden, after a thorough examination of the archives suggests that Boerhaave Sr. had a pied-à-terre in the Breestraat; for in 1683 Herman is also mentioned in connection with freedom of excise duties, as living with his father in the Breestraat. Two of his half-brothers were born and baptised in Leiden; his father died there, and only afterwards the body was brought to Voorhout. Hence Downer suggests that this pied-à-terre should be sought in the house of the physician Franciscus Gomarus, an uncle of Ewout Gomarus, who had married the sister of Herman's stepmother, Eva Dubois. Franciscus Gomarus had a house on the Eastern corner of the Vrouwensteeg. It could be added that Franciscus Gomarus could have been the Leiden physician who was expected to treat Herman more cheaply; if this is right, however, his medical advice did not benefit Herman. In the end the latter cured himself with the help of his own urine and salt. It was only in his first year at the University that the disease was completely healed.

Among his classmates several sons of notables in and outside Leiden were to be found: high society was well represented in the school. At the end of 1682 Herman received the first prize and was promoted to the second grade. Now he was in the form of the deputy headmaster, Lucas van Rijp. At the end of each grade there followed an examination, part of which was public. The summer examination was held on June 10, and was followed by a holiday of three weeks; in winter the examination took place on December 10, again to be followed by a holiday of three weeks. At the examination of June 1683 Herman again received a first prize, and was promoted to the class of the headmaster Winschooten. The certificate attendant on this prize has been preserved and rests at the Koninklijke Bibliotheek in The Hague. The certificate has been signed by three 'scholarchs': namely Professor Jacobus Le Mort, who in 1718 would be succeeded by Herman in the Chair of Chemistry; Professor Burchard de Volder, who was to be Herman's teacher of physics at the University; and Daniël van Alphen, one of the four burgomasters of Leiden, who was to become Secretary to the Board of Governors of the University in 1687. The two last named were men to whom Herman in the future was to be greatly indebted.

On November 12, 1683 Herman suffered a heavy loss: his father died. On the preceding day the latter had summoned the notary Jacobus van der Stoffe, living in the Breestraat, to his sickbed in order to arrange for the guardianship of his children. The guardians appointed were the Rev. Theodorus van der Lee, a Leiden minister, and the merchant Pieter van der Deijster. It is a pity that their precise relationship with the family Boerhaave could not be ascertained. It was also laid down that if the wife of the Rev. Boerhaave would survive her husband, she was to educate not only her own children but also all the children of his earlier marriage. She did survive him, and has performed this task in an exemplary manner. Herman had a deep affection for his father, and cherished him in his memory to the end of his own life, not only because of his intellect and erudition, but also because of his character.

Herman's financial situation was not improved by this event. He received his statutory portion of the estate, but that was not much – not sufficient to pay for his further studies. He asked his guardians for permission to spend his inheritance on his studies as far as it would go. He also asked their consent for his plan to begin his University studies only in September 1684, instead of January. That consent was given, and so he remained for yet another term of six months with Winschooten. He still suffered much pain from the swelling on his thigh.

Another person to whom he was greatly indebted was the Rev. Jakob Trigland, Professor of Theology (1652-1705), who had left Utrecht for Leiden. He was the son of the well-known Trigland who had played such an important role during the Synod of Dordt, and who had been an intimate friend of Herman's father. Trigland felt obliged to concern himself with the fate of the orphaned Herman; he helped him by word and deed, and introduced him to Van Alphen, already mentioned, who in his turn regularly gave support to Herman when this was needed.

To summarise: the two years spent by Herman at the grammar school certainly have not been time wasted; neither with regard to his education, nor with regard to his social contacts.    D.E.K.

# 4. STUDENT AT THE UNIVERSITY

B oerhaave has studied at the University of Leiden from 1684 to
1693. During the first years of this period he attended the lectures
of well-known Professors of Theology and Philosophy. Such lectures
were given in the University building on the Rapenburg. This was the
centre of the University; all important activities and events took place
here.

Originally, the building was used as a convent church, founded in
1490 for the Dominican nuns, the so-called 'White Nuns'. In the time
of the Reformation most convents fell into disrepair, the buildings
were emptied, and the greater part of them was taken over by the
authorities of the towns. In 1581 the domicile of the University was
transferred from the church of the 'Faliede Begijnen' to this convent
of the White Nuns. According to the author of the chronicles of
Leiden J.J. Orlers, it was 'larger and more convenient, built along a
distinguished broad street, and a beautiful wide canal, planted on
each side with tall and large lime-trees; in summertime it is very
pleasant to walk under them'.

The building was adapted to its new destiny as a set of lecture
rooms: in the large space of the chapel an in-between floor was
constructed, and a partition: on one side of the latter one finds what
is now called the 'Vaulted Room' and upstairs the present Room of
the Senate; on the other side there is the Great Auditorium (Hall) and
above that on the first floor the Small Auditorium.

In the past the Great Auditorium, the imposing hall downstairs,
was called the *Auditorium Theologicum*. Disputations were held here
*ex cathedra* by students, under the direction of the Professor.

The first disputation held here by Boerhaave had a subject from
the field of science. Professor Wolferd Senguerd was in charge –
experimental philosophy was among the subjects he taught. In this
disputation Boerhaave upheld a physical thesis, *De cohaesione cor-
porum* (On the cohesion of particles in a substance). In 1689 he also
began to study mathematics and attended the lectures of Burchard de
Volder. These lectures were given in the *Auditorium Medicum*, which
is at present the Senate's Room. Among Boerhaave's teachers Burchard de Volder was one of his favourites. In 1674 De Volder had
visited England, and it is probable that there he already got into touch
with Isaac Newton. After his return he had obtained the consent of

the Board of Governors for to set up a laboratory for experimental physics of the kind he had become acquainted with in England. For this purpose, then, a little building had been fitted up in 1675, which was situated in the Nonnensteeg, next-door to the official residence of the Professor of Botany. This building became the *Laboratorium Physicum*, where Boerhaave was to work regularly. As such it has remained in use up to 1825.

In 1690 Boerhaave took his degree in philosophy, and from now on he devoted all his energy to his theological studies. He attended lectures on the Hebrew and Chaldean languages, as well as on ecclesiastical history. Furthermore he studied at home the Bible and the writings of the Church Fathers intensively. After six years of study, however, he had no longer the financial means at his disposal

10. The University building on the Rapenburg. From: *Les Délices de Leide.* Anonymous (1712).

which were needed to complete his ambitious study programme. He began therefore to teach mathematics to some 'select youths'. This attracted the attention of Johan van den Bergh, the Secretary of the Board of Governors of the University.

It was he who saw to it that Boerhaave was entrusted with the supervision of the changes to be made in the University Library, which related to the purchase of a large collection of books from England. For this the student Boerhaave received a financial remuneration, to be used for the expenses of his studies.

From 1691 to 1693, then, Boerhaave completed his medical studies. Indubitably, he amassed the greater part of his knowledge from the perusal of books, and attending a few public dissections in the Anatomical Theatre performed by Antonius Nuck, who unfortunately died in 1692. In the field of anatomy Boerhaave probably acquired most of his knowledge from the Amsterdam scientist Frederik Ruysch; in his house Boerhaave was a regular and valued visitor. He even spent his holidays there! He did not attend the lectures of the Leiden Professors of Botany, Anatomy, and Medicine. Moreover, he kept wholly aloof from the Cartesian concepts of illness, prevailing in that period. Neither did he accompany the town surgeons or physicians on their visits to patients, as was still something of a custom in those days. And after the death of Professor Lucas Schacht in 1689 the clinical teaching in the Caecilia Hospital had greatly deteriorated; the Governors of the University complained that 'more healthy persons than sick ones were lying in the beds', and, even worse, notwithstanding repeated summonses the Professors appointed refused to perform their duties in the Hospital. It seems very probable, then, that during his medical studies and even for a long time afterwards Boerhaave has almost never visited the Caecilia Hospital. Only after 1714, when he was put in charge of the clinical teaching, Boerhaave has taken on the *collegium medico-practicum* (practical demonstrations of medicine) in the hospital.

He spent more time on chemistry, which he studied together with his brother Jacobus, and probably with the assistance of the Leiden apothecary David Stam. The latter had been a student of Boerhaave's famous predecessor Franciscus de le Boë, Sylvius, and had carried out experiments together with his teacher. Boerhaave has always held a high opinion of chemistry: *chemiam diem et noctem exercuit*, (he studied chemistry by night and day), as he says in his autobiographical notes. It seems probable that he carried out his chemical experiments at home in the Begijnhof.

To summarise, then: The University itself, the *Theatrum Physicum* and *Theatrum Anatomicum*, together with the University Library, have been the most important locations where Boerhaave has worked during his years of study.

A.M.L.-E.

## 5. LIVING IN THE BEGIJNHOF

During Boerhaave's early years of study he continued to live in the Breestraat with his 'uncle' Ewout Gomarus. In 1686 his name is again to be found in the register of members of the University exempted from paying the tax on beer. His host seems to have stocked a considerable amount of beer, to judge from the issue of 'vrijcelen', little vouchers for the purchase of a cask of beer free from tax. It seems probable that several inhabitants of the house joined in drinking this beer. In the years from 1690 onwards Boerhaave is each time registered as 'living with the widow of the Rev. Boerhaven' up to 1701, when his name was transferred from the register of students to that of the University lecturers. In this his name is regularly given without an address, and no purchases of tax-free beer are mentioned; this was not rare among students and Professors.

11. The Begijnhof with the gate giving on to the Rapenburg. Coloured drawing by J. Timmerman (ca. 1787).

According to the accounts of the Begijnhof it was in May 1668 that Hfl.50,– was for the first time received 'from Mrs. Boerhaven', *loco* (instead of) Abraham Bulaert for a year's rent'; it follows that she will have moved into the small house of no. 30 in May, 1687. 'Ms. Boeraven' faithfully continued to pay that rent until 1695. It even happened at times that she advanced some money: the account of 1690 mentions 'Hfl. 10,– paid to Eva Boerhaven for an advance on repairs done in the house no. 30'. The account of 1695 states that from May 1, 1694 onwards this house was let to the children of Jacob Voorn (who, incidentally, had to pay no more than Hfl. 30,– a year). The family Boerhaave had moved into the house no. 31 – which actually consisted of a combination of the numbers 31 and 32, and which had

12. The Gate of the Begijnhof. Coloured drawing by J.J. Bijlaart (ca. 1770).

13. The Faliede Begijnkerk with the entrance of the *Theatrum Anatomicum* on the north-west side, and the entrance of the Library via the stairs in the tower. Coloured drawing by J.J. Bijlaert (ca. 1770).

earlier been let to the widow of the Rev. Belcampius. This house may have been somewhat larger or better, for the annual rent came to Hfl. 63,–. From that year onwards there were no more changes; each year the widow Boerhaave faithfully paid this sum of Hfl. 63,–.

In the account of 1702 the word 'Mrs.' was erased and 'Mr.' was substituted; naturally, because it is Herman who is referred to here, being the new head of the family after the death of his stepmother. The account for 1706 therefore explicitly mentions: Mr. Hermanus Boerhaven. Herman continued to live here until May 1708, for in the account for 1709 it is 'Miss. Catarina Sijen', who is referred to as the tenant for Hfl. 63,–; she was born in 1685, the daughter of Johannes Louis Sijen and Cornelia Voorn.

14.    The Begijnhof. Ground plan by J. van Hout (ca. 1595).

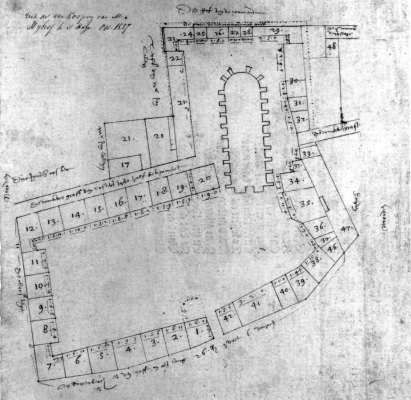

Now what was this Begijnhof (beguinage) like, and why has Herman lived there so long, even after his stepmother had died? The 'Grote-, St. Agnes-, or Gefalijde Begijnhof' (or, sometimes: 'Bagijn-hof') was founded some time before 1293 on a location which is now part of the Pieterskerkplein. Because the Pieterskerk and the attendant graveyard were continually enlarged, after 1400 the beguinage had to disappear. A new terrain was bought at the corner of the Rapenburg and what afterwards became the Kloksteeg; on this a much more spacious beguinage was built. There was even room for a large chapel, in which one could be buried as well – in that period this was a boon only rarely conferred by the church wardens and parish priests of the Pieterskerk, who carefully safeguarded their own privileges in this respect.

The small houses were the private property of the beguines, although there were a number of special restrictive stipulations. After the Reformation the spiritual institute of the beguinage was abolished; the town took over. From that time onwards the Town Council appointed two governors and a steward, who collected the revenues of the houses, took care of the necessary repairs, and paid other expenses. It goes without saying that the number of beguines steadily diminished. As soon as one of them died or departed, the town bought or expropriated the house in which she had lived; hence in a relatively short period after 1572 the town obtained possession of the greater part of the houses. And what was the policy of the governors, appointed by the town, with regard to those vacated houses?

In 1577, only two years after its foundation, the University was obliged to leave the Convent of St. Barbara on the Rapenburg (on the place where now the houses nrs. 4-10 are to be found), in order to make room for the Prinsenhof. The church of the Begijnhof was chosen as its new accommodation. And because now most lectures and other University activities took place in the Begijnhof, and a large majority of the newly-appointed Professors did not already live in Leiden but came from elsewhere, it was not to be wondered at that a house in the Begijnhof was offered to them, so that they did not have long to seek for a suitable place to live. There they had, moreover, all facilities of the University ready to hand. Another advantage was that it enabled the town administration to some extent to put a check on the rents which on the free market were steadily rising. The town had a crucial interest in the flourishing of the University – this was reflected in the fact that all four burgomasters were among its Governors, as against a minority of three, appointed by the States of Holland; moreover, up to 1592 the Town Clerk Jan van Hout also served as the Secretary of the University's Board of Governors.

Van Hout was also one of the regents of the Begijnhof, and we owe it to his great meticulousness that all his accounts of the beguinage are now in the possession of the Town Archive. With the Begijnhof he held a winning card in his attempts to entice renowned Professors to come to Leiden. He could keep their rent low, or even wholly remit it. Hence a considerable number of famous Professors has lived in the Begijnhof. There was one drawback, however: the houses of the Begijnhof were rather small; and in that period it was in particular the Professors who often had large libraries and other collections, which took up a lot of room. Several Professors, moreover, had large families, which also had their requirements; or – if the Professors were already so old that their children were on their own – they earned an additional income by taking in students as lodgers. Al-

15.   The Faliede Begijnkerk (rear view; in its present condition). Photograph by J. Lens (1982).

though not all Professors felt like giving house-room to students, it was a recurrent phenomenon. In such cases even a combination of two of the small houses did not suffice. And after some years a considerable part of the learned gentlemen regarded living in the Begijnhof as somewhat beneath them. As soon as in 1581 the University was moved to the convent of the White Nuns on the Rapenburg, this street along the canal became a popular locality for their houses. The houses there were much larger, and the Professors preferred also to live close to one another here. Yet the Begijnhof still remained popular as an abode for Professors as well – which was probably due to the fact that the University Library was housed in its church. The University Librarian Professor Daniel Heinsius, for instance, had lived for some years in the Begijnhof, and this should probably be ascribed to the fact that the Library was nearby.

The widow Boerhaave-du Bois with her large family chose to live in the Begijnhof because Herman's studies were located in Leiden. As has been said already, the family Boerhaave had an abode both in Leiden and in Voorhout. When Herman's father, the Rev. Jacobus Boerhaave, died (shortly before November 13, 1683) there were actually no more grounds for keeping the vicarage in Voorhout on; moreover, this house may well have been claimed by a new vicar. It is not clear, however, where the widow has lived up to 1687. It may be taken for granted that Herman soon joined the family when his stepmother had moved to the Begijnhof. For a future theologian and physician the close vicinity of the Library and the Anatomical Theatre was certainly a great attraction! This may also have been the crucial argument for Boerhaave's decision to continue to stay with the remnant of the family after the death of Mrs. Boerhaave-du Bois (shortly before October 28, 1702), when he could easily have resolved to buy a somewhat better and larger house elsewhere. On the other hand, the move from the Begijnhof to the official residence in the Nonnensteeg was but logical; not only was this house free of rent, but in 1709 little was still left of the family's original constitution.

From 1701 onwards, after his appointment as a University lecturer, Boerhaave had a better position. Apart from his lessons in mathematics he now also taught chemistry and anatomy, with the consent of the University's Governors. With regard to chemistry Boerhaave even managed to demonstrate experiments in his own home. The Professor of Chemistry, Jacobus Le Mort, was not very pleased with this state of affairs; in his diary the student Albrecht von Haller writes that in this period Boerhaave managed to attract most of Le Mort's students to his own lectures. Boerhaave's approach in teaching anatomy is not clear. His friend and teacher Frederik Ruysch may have presented him with a number of specimens. It is, moreover, possible that he has performed a few public dissections in the Theatre, to which the authorities turned a blind eye. For the Professor Govert Bidloo, who was the personal physician of the King-Stadtholder William III, lived most of the time in England, and neglected his University duties. For that reason the Governors also gave the opportunity to other people to use the Theatre for teaching purposes. In this time Boerhaave has also written a simple manual for dissecting the cavities of thorax and abdomen, which is still preserved among his posthumous manuscripts.

With regard to the kind of neighbours of the family Boerhaave in the Begijnhof, it would lead us too far afield to enumerate all changes among them. But studying, for instance, a little list drawn up in 1701 gives a good impression of such people. Many houses of the original number of 48 were already sold or joined together; there remained 33 houses, which were mainly occupied by people of rather humble descent; certainly not persons with a university education. For instance, the sextoness of the English Church lived in no. 15, the children of the bookseller Jacob Voorn in no. 30, next-door to the family Boerhaave. Among the tenants the female element predominated; six of these women are referred to as being widows. One of them, who lived in no. 42, was also the gatekeeper of the Begijnhof. At that time the 'ghetto of the learned' was already definitely a thing of the past. The houses still available were sold on a public auction in 1762; the remaining money was kept in a separate account until 1802, when it disappeared without leaving a trace in the bottomless pit of the municipal treasury. With a few exceptions all the houses of the Begijnhof have disappeared, owing to the continuously expanding buildings of the University Library. On this spot a part of the church is all that remains of the original Begijnhof.                P.J.M.d.B.

47

## 6. THE THEATRUM ANATOMICUM OR DISSECTING ROOM 1687 – 1709

Little remains now of the former 'Faliede Begijnhof'; the small houses in which the family Boerhaave lived have disappeared. Even so, a remnant of the chapel can still be seen, and it is precisely that part in which in the past the *Theatrum Anatomicum* has been constructed. At the time this was a famous hall for public dissections of the Medical Faculty.

On the Rapenburg, in the neighbourhood of the Kloksteeg, one now comes upon a passage ending in a cul-de-sac, which runs past the Garden of the State Herbarium (formerly the University Library), and which is labelled 'Begijnhof'. Upon entering this one sees a spacious enclosed garden; in this, to the right, behind the bicycle-shed, the house no. 31 has stood, where Boerhaave lived during a long period; to the left, however, one can still very clearly discern the (southern) wall of the old chapel; its buttresses make it easily recognisable.

In this chapter we shall focus on the Anatomical Theatre which in the past was housed in this chapel, and we shall describe how this was built into it. Already in the end of 1591 the work had begun to make the chapel ready for the Anatomical Theatre, mentioned above, and for a library; a wall was erected which was to divide the nave in two. The western half, in which the tower also stood, was divided horizontally by constructing an in-between floor, halfway the chapel's height. By means of this an upper storey was created, which was fitted out as the library. Underneath some rooms were made; one of them was to be used for many years as the English Church. The church windows were divided in two; this is clearly discernible in some representations (fig. 13). The part on the eastern side of the dividing wall, reserved for the Anatomical Theatre, was so large that a set of circular wooden galleries could be constructed in it; this was supported by a floor on a height of 2.20 metres above the ground level. Under that gallery some workrooms and storage rooms had been fitted up. On a later floor plan these have been labelled 'Rooms for preliminary treatment of specimens'. Some small rooms of (probably ancient) lean-to houses, built against the chapel wall, which could be entered from within the chapel, were also incorporated.

Together these buildings constituted the Anatomical Theatre, which was to serve the Medical Faculty: appropriate for anatomical and chirurgical demonstrations, anatomical research and dissections, storage of anatomical specimens, instruments, a medical library, and a collection of prints. To begin with, the Guild of Surgeons also had its domicile here, but in Boerhaave's time the surgeons had an accommodation elsewhere in the town.

This Anatomical Theatre, then, which was finished in 1592, contained a representative room, the large hall for dissections with its wooden galleries which was called the *Theatrum Anatomicum,* or 'Dissecting Room', and became very well known, mainly because of its special structure. This structure was felt to be classical; as it has been put by Orlers: 'Built in the manner of the ancient Roman Theatres'.

It looked indeed like a miniature theatre, with circular galleries, which were steeply rising one above the other in the way of an amphitheatre, and centring around a table which was suitable for dissecting the human body upon it for demonstrations, giving visual aid to the lectures on anatomy and surgery for both medical students and the surgeons.

The Dissecting Room took up the entire breadth of the chapel, 9.80 metres, and had a depth of approximately 9 metres. The supporting floor, on which the dissecting table also stood, has already been mentioned; from this floor upwards the hall had a height of more than 12 metres up to the highest point of the old vaulted ceiling. It is certain that it was well-lighted: the upper parts of all church windows were still intact, and provided with clear windowpanes. The Dissecting Room, then, had good light on three sides. It must have been a beautiful sight. A print made in 1711 gives something of an impression of this (fig. 16).

That was the beginning in 1592, thanks to the initiative and the inspiring direction of Professor Pieter Paaw (Pavius). He was the first anatomist who performed public dissections in this theatre, and who mounted skeletons for teaching purposes, both of humans and of animals. He ordered them to be arranged on the guard-rails of the galleries in the Theatre, some on little shelves (in his writings Paaw calls then 'luifkens'), some on iron spills which pierced the guardrails. In 1600 the series of animal skeletons had grown to approximately seventeen specimens, according to Paaw's first enumeration. During the summer the exposition was present in the theatre; in wintertime many skeletons were transferred to the University building and stored there, or used for teaching. Then the Dissecting Room was free and available for the anatomical lectures, at which at least two hundred spectators could be present.

50

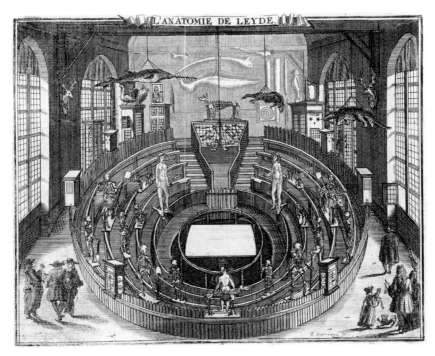

16. The Anatomical Theatre, with embalmed humans and animals, skeletons, and curiosities on display. Engraving by J. Harrewijn (1711).

Gradually this collection of skeletons developed into a full-scale museum, to which afterwards quite different and very heterogeneous objects were added. And with this we touch upon one of the most extraordinary and fascinating histories within this town: the coming into being and flourishing of a world-famous collection in the Anatomical Theatre in Leiden. This collection, then, comprehended many curiosities ('rarities' as they were called in the past). After two centuries, however, this has disappeared so imperceptibly from the former chapel of the Begijnhof, that nowadays it can hardly be imagined.

Paaw administered yet another University museum, however. In 1600 a gallery had been built in the Botanical Garden; one of its purposes was to winter plants. Here natural and ethnographic objects were displayed as well. No distinction was made as yet between natural history and ethnography; everything was a curiosity – which

51

here also meant: rare and often exotic collector's items. To some extent Paaw distinguished between such categories: natural and ethnographic items were put in the Botanical Garden with the plants, whereas all anatomical specimens were to enrich the collection in the Dissecting Room. Afterwards the policy with regard to exposing and collecting items was less carefully kept apart. This happened after Paaw's death, when the Botanical Garden and the Anatomical Institute were put under separate management.

Now, however, we shall briefly trace the beginning and growth of the collection of curiosities in the Anatomical Theatre. The first record dates from 1594, when the *rift*, 'skeleton', is mentioned in writing. It seems that only a single specimen was available! Afterwards Paaw was very diligently dissecting and mounting specimens, as has been said already, and used the large Dissecting Room as an exhibition space. He may also have received some donations as, for instance, some bones of a large sperm whale, which had been washed ashore near Katwijk in 1598; they were fastened to the wall.

From his own possessions Paaw contributed a number of stag's heads, which were to adorn the piers between the windows. They were made of wood, with real antlers. Moreover, the decoration became more elaborate. In 1609 a first representation of the whole was made, entitled *Amphitheatrum Anatomicum Lugduno Batavorum* (Anatomical Theatre in Leiden). The picture shows that by that time an evidently moralising element had been visualised. The skeletons now were arranged as in a veritable *danse macabre*. On banners and decorative plates maxims could be read on the 'fragility and insignificance of human bodies' (according to Orlers).

After Paaw's death in 1617, however, exotic objects began to pour into the Anatomical Theatre as well, as if a rivalry with the gallery in the Botanical Garden was to be set up. And anyway the amount of curiosities was large: gifts for the University came from far and wide, donated by travellers or distant connections: animal preparations, pieces of coral, minerals, antique and ethnographic objects, Egyptian mummies, jewels, arms, and musical instruments.

In the first decades of the seventeenth century the summer display of the skeletons evidently preserved its moralising message, even if, as time went by, the banners disappeared. But maxims hanging on the wall, prints and pictures, which had been introduced by Paaw's successor Ottho Heurnius, still reminded the spectator of life's vanity. The attendants of the Theatre, who showed visitors around, seem

17. The *Theatrum Anatomicum*. A reconstruction in the Museum Boerhaave (1989).

in their own way also to have emphasised that crime will be punished: the skeletons, which before symbolised death in a gloomy but quiet way, now were explicitly identified as the mortal remains of criminals, whose offences were also enumerated. In the second half of the seventeenth century, then, the guides in the Dissecting Room surely emphasised an element of horror.

The sum total of the collection increased so much within a few years that additional cupboards and showcases were installed, to begin with on the topmost gallery of the Theatre. It was in particular the most precious objects which were safely put away there. But soon the theatre was full of rare objects – put in the sloping space beneath the wooden galleries, in a small side room, and in the hallway on the ground level. They attracted a good deal of attention. Some of the travel books or guides, published in that period, were very popular and in these the collection of rare items was often mentioned. The Anatomical Theatre in Leiden became internationally known and famous. Tourists came flocking in. In the *Reys-Boeck door de Vereenigde Nederlanden* (1689), a kind of tourist guide, for instance it is said that there 'so many beautiful and strange objects are to be seen that only an Argus would be able to count them all'.

From 1699 onwards a catalogue of them was printed in Dutch, afterwards followed by Latin, English, and French versions.

CATALOGUS

Van alle de principaelfte

RARITEYTEN

die op de

ANATOMIE-
KAMER

Binnen de Stad LEYDEN
vertoont worden.

*Geftelt in ordre volgens de plaetfen
daer de felve ftaen.*

TOT LEYDEN,
By J. VOORN, Boeckverkooper, 1690.

18.   Title page of the catalogue of the objects in the *Theatrum Anatomicum*. (J. Voorn, 1690).

This was the overall situation with which Herman Boerhaave must have become acquainted, when he came to live almost directly across the Theatre, on the Faliede Begijnhof. It may be gathered from his writings that already during his theological studies he has visited the Theatre. Herman had very varied interests – that follows from the fact that he was a man of wide reading – and it is probable that he will have looked around, fascinated and full of respect, impressed by God's marvellous world. It is wholly in accordance with the spirit of the age that an introductory poem in the catalogue admonishes the visitor to 'praise his Lord, who has created all'. Herman must not only have gained an impression of the vast dimensions of the world, but also have become aware of the fact that all these far-away countries were accessible from Holland, via journeys over land and sea, and our expanding trading companies. In those days the horizon of Holland was enormously wide, and this is mirrored in the Anatomical Theatre, a world in miniature.

( 9 )

32 't Hooft van een jonge Olijphant.
33 Een Vraet.
34 Een vreemde Zee-vis.
35 Een Zee-egel.
36 't Hooft van een wildt Vercken.
37 't Geraemte van een Kievit.
38 Een beeft genaemt Taton, door Pr. Maurits.
39 een Egel.
40 De Snuyt van een Zaeg-vis.
41 't Hooft van een Zee-koe.
42 De Roede van een Walvis.
43 't Vel van een Man, als Zeem-leer bereyt.
44 't Gedarmte van een Man.
45 Een Tijger uyt Oost-Indien, door D. P. de Carpentier, Gouverneur in Indien.
46 't Conterfeytfel van een Boer uyt Pruyffen, die een mes van 10. duym inflikte, het welke weder uyt de maeg is gefneden, ende heeft nogh 8. jaer daar na geleeft, D. Danielis Beckheri.
47 Een vis dewelcke inde Haerlemmermeer gevangen is.
48 Een Luyaert, door Prins Maurits.
49 Twee Beenen met de Rugge-graet aan malkanderen gegroeyt.
50 Een Huis gelijk men in Noorweegen maeckt van balcken, fonder kalck ende fteen.
* 50 Een ftuk van de baart van een Wal-vis, gevange voor Zirckzee.

A 5     51 Den

( 10 )

51 Den baert van een jonge Walvis.
52 Seven Wervel-beenen met het Gemachtbeen, vers te famen gegroeyt.
53 Het Geraemte van een Arent.
54 Den Snuyt van een Zaeg-vis.
55 Een Stoel uyt de wortel van een boom zijnde foo gewaffchen, uit Amboina, door D. Petris de Carpentier.
56 Een Roch uyt Angola.
57 De Blaes van een Menfch, daar 4. ftoop nat in gaat.
58 Een Mieren-eeter, door Prins Maurits.
59 Een Luypaert.
60 Een Crocodil, door Prins Maurits.
61 Een Hemdt van Menfchen darmen, door Mr. Johannis a Leeuwen.
62 Eenige Vellen van Tijgers, door Pr. Maurits.
63 Het Vel van een Man, bereyt als Hoorn perkement.
64 't Geraemte van een Das.
65 Een Inftrument Gloffoconium genaemt.
66 Een groote Kreeft uit Oost-Indien.
67 Een Civet-Cat, door de Hr. ende Mr. Theod. Gool.
98 Een Zee-hont.
66 Het vel van een Enkhoorntje uit Ooftindien.
70 't Vel van een groote Slange.
71 't Gedarmte ende Maag van een Menfch.

72 Een

19.   The 'Prussian knife-eater'; entered here under nr. 46 in the Catalogue (1690).

All this may be somewhat speculative, however. There is only one reliable piece of evidence: when Boerhaave began his medical studies 'He assiduously attended the public dissections of the famous Nuck in the Dissection Room', according to his biographer Schultens. The anatomist Antonius Nuck performed these public dissections between 1687 and 1692. Although Boerhaave in his writings respectfully referred to Nuck's anatomical technique, and in particular to his injections of mercury in the lymphatic system, he did nowhere in his writings pay special attention to the layout and the curiosities in the Theatre itself.

Even so, it is not without interest to investigate what there was to be seen in the Anatomical Theatre during the more than twenty years that Boerhaave lived in its immediate neighbourhood; but for this we must turn to another source. Analysing an entire catalogue as, for instance, the one published by J. Voorn in 1690, containing approximately 300 items, would take up too much space here; but some few pages have been copied, to convey a general impression (figs. 19).

As has already been said, the eldest catalogue known to us dates from 1669. This was compiled by the *custos*, (attendant) of the Anatomical Theatre, Hendrik Cramer. Many editions followed, each time published by the successive *custodes*, like Jacob Voorn, already mentioned, (who performed this task from 1682 to 1692), and his successor Gerrit Blancke, who has also lived in the Faliede Begijnhof. Publication of the catalogue must have been a private initiative of those *custodes*. The sale of the work procured an additional income for them. The price was 4 five-cent pieces, as has been noted by an Englishman in 1687.

Now when one compares all known editions it becomes evident that there have been few changes in the arrangement and content of the collection of curiosities between 1669 and 1716, when the last version known to us was published. One may conclude that, generally speaking, the presentation of that museum in the Dissecting Room was already stabilised in 1669, and was to remain all but unchanged during many years.

Paaw and Heurnius had themselves built up the collections, and set their stamp upon it; but gradually the immediate supervision passed to a great extent into the hands of the attendant of the anatomy, who gained a considerable degree of autonomy in his policy, or rather management, with regard to the collection which provided him with a number of emoluments. The visitor, for instance, might give him a guilder by way of a tip or entrance fee; he

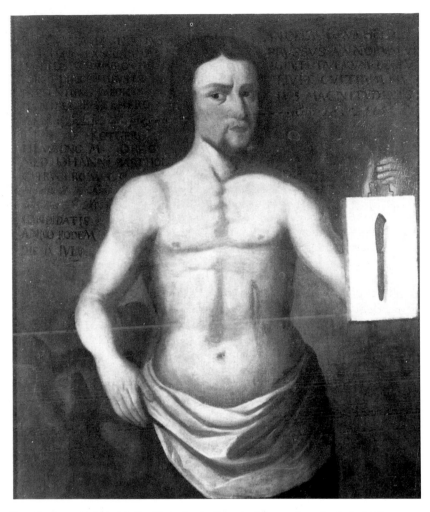

20. Andreas Grünheid, the 'Prussian knife-eater' from whose body in 1635
a knife, which he had swallowed, was removed. Anonymous painting,
which in 1639 was presented to the *Theatrum Anatomicum*.

bought a catalogue. It was in the interest of the attendant of Anatomy,
then, that there were as few changes as possible in the famous and
much visited expositions in the Dissecting Room.

One need not wonder that the influence of the Professor of Anatomy was less noticeable in this respect. The teaching was his main concern, as well as public dissections and, if possible, research (the latter was probably carried out in the 'Rooms for Preparing'). What is significant in this respect is the character of the collection of specimens of J.J. Rau, who occupied the Chair of Anatomy at the University of Leiden from 1713 onwards. This exceptionally fine collection of specimens in methylated spirits, which at his death was bequeathed to the University, was not even mentioned in the catalogues of the attendant of the Anatomy. Indeed, from the first decade of the eighteenth century onwards a distinction may be made between a scientific collection, like that of Rau, and that of the old 'curiosities'. The Dutch 'rariteit' which should be related to the Latin *rarus*, English 'rare', gradually comes to mean 'oddities': something slightly ridiculous – objects mainly worth seeing for rustic girls, to quote Haller. For in his diary he writes: 'In the summer it [the Theatre] is everywhere crammed with human and animal skeletons and all kinds of curiosities, which are viewed with attention by rustic girls'. And afterwards in a survey he writes: 'All kinds of rare items are present there, the finest thing is the treasure of specimens of Rau; among them the bones in particular are marvellously beautiful. Such are the objects one sees here, which even a rustic girl would not forget'.

In Boerhaave's time, then, the ancient collection in the Anatomical Theatre appears gradually to have become less important, after the University had acquired the scientific collection of Rau. In Boerhaave's youth anatomical work could still be carried out in the setting of allegorical representations, exotic objects, and marvellous rarities in a world-wide perspective. But a reversal was on its way, which took place during his professorate.

It cannot be doubted that Boerhaave was influenced by this change; and he has done his part in removing the allegorical elements from medicine. In this he was supported by his young colleague Bernhard Siegfried Albinus, who was to lead the science of anatomy in a wholly new direction.

The old collection, on the other hand, continued to exist separately and almost on its own, almost as a tourist attraction pure and simple, with a diminishing importance for the contemporary physicians. Apart from that a scientific collection came into being, which was to be the nucleus of what was afterwards proudly labelled as the 'Anatomical Collection'. Both processes illuminate a development which took place in the historical period of Herman Boerhaave's life and work. Indeed, this development itself is an outstanding illustration of those general changes in mentality, which at times have been called the 'crisis of European thought', and which took place, roughly, in those years between 1680 and 1715.                    A.J.F.G.

## 7. THE LIBRARY

As we have seen, the upper storey of the church of the 'Faliede Begijnen' was from 1593 onwards in use as an accommodation for the University Library. In 1594 it had twelve reading desks; above them shelves had been fitted up for the folio volumes. Each folio was fastened with a chain to an iron rod with a padlock. On the south-west side of the Library a trapdoor with a pulley had been put in, to hoist up books in baskets from the ground level. Against the wall which divided the Library from the Anatomical Theatre a chimney was installed which had a breadth of two and a half metres, with a large chimney-breast.

The only room which was still in use for religious purposes was below the Library. This was the so-called English Church. From 1595 onwards the Board of Governors of the University made plans to have a large staircase built in the south-western corner of this church, that is to say, under the trapdoor and leading up to the Library; for members of the University who were somewhat portly were unable to pass one another on the narrow stairs in the small tower.

In 1690 an important event took place in the Library. On October 21 of that year a flat-bottomed barge, a so-called 'Kaegh', was moored

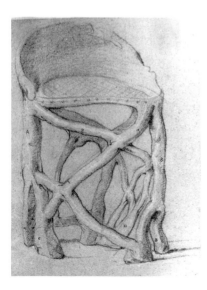

21. A chair made from the root of a tree from Ambon. Pastel drawing by M. Saeghmolen (ca. 1650). See nr. 55 of the Catalogue (fig. 19).

61

in the canal of the Rapenburg under the autumnal trees. Labourers were busy unloading 34 chests from it; these were carried to the church. The work was supervised by an elegantly dressed young man, who closely watched the activities of the workmen. It was evident from his attitude and behaviour that he was entrusted with an important task. Indeed, Mr. Johan van den Bergh, Secretary of the dignified Board of Governors of the University, was very much aware of this. But the inhabitants of Leiden in general also realised that this was a momentous event! The issue at hand was an important purchase for the Library. This was to be enriched with the most valuable collection which at any time had been bought by the University: the collection of books and manuscripts, accumulated by Isaac Vossius. In 1689 Vossius lived in England as a Canon of Windsor and caretaker of a famous library, which he had been collecting initially by order of Queen Christina of Sweden.

22.    The University Library. From: *Les Délices de Leide*. Anonymous (1712).

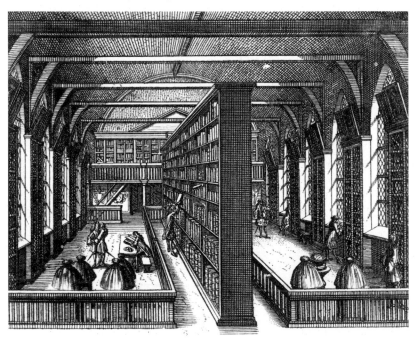

The books had been shipped in England. Van den Bergh had journeyed to Amsterdam in order to oversee the further transport from there. The trapdoor in the Library had been especially enlarged for the chests; moreover, after the transport the door of the Library was to be secured with two double locks 'in order that nobody could gain access to them'.

In the Library the reading desks had been pushed to the wall, to make room for trestles on which the books were to be unpacked. In the middle of the hall double bookcases were to be installed, and for the walls cases with netting.

Two Professors were given the task of ordering and checking the books. However, they urgently needed help for examining, registering, and placing the collection.

On October 18, 1691, then, the 'student Herman Boerhaave' together with the son of the *custos* of the Anatomical Theatre was appointed to help with the work. It was a complete chaos: everywhere books lay scattered. By now the Library had already been closed for students for more than a year. The alterations had to be finished first, so that the books could be placed in the new bookcases. Duplicates had to be put in a separate case, which would be nailed up and so could be sold in its entirety at some later time.

When the alterations were finished Boerhaave could begin with the checking. In this he was assisted by a former monk from France, Casimir Oudijn, who had much expert knowledge of manuscripts. The Professor of Ecclesiastical History, F. Spanheim, and Johan van den Bergh had taken him under their protection when he had fled from France for religious reasons.

Regrettably, in March 1691 it had already become apparent that the contents of the chests did not correspond with the list of books, based on Isaac Vossius' catalogue. A process against the heirs of Vossius about missing books and manuscripts, which was to drag on almost endlessly, was still in store for the Governors of the University of Leiden. But Boerhaave enjoyed a privileged position: he had free access to the Library and could study the books to his heart's content, whereas his fellow-students found the door closed! In June 1692 the catalogue was finished, the books had been put in order, and the duplicates thrown out. In November 1692 Boerhaave received Hfl. 200,– for his labours, but it may safely be assumed that his year in the Library has enriched him in far more ways.

Boerhaave probably has mainly occupied himself with the printed works. In his time these were not as highly esteemed as manuscripts.

In a University town like Leiden printers and booksellers were as thick as flies. It was not in keeping with the Governors' policy to spend more than Hfl. 300,– a year on the purchase of new books, and the ones bought were merely destined to fill the 'most shocking gaps' for the separate faculties. It need not to be wondered at, then, that Boerhaave's student Albrecht von Haller in 1726 was to complain that he had not witnessed a single acquisition during his stay in Leiden.

In the Vossius collection, however, many good editions of modern works, of English scientists in particular, were represented. To mention only a single instance: the first edition of Isaac Newton's *Philosophiae Naturalis Principia Mathematica*, which had been published as recently as 1687 in a limited number of copies, was present among the mathematical books. Boerhaave has certainly not failed to notice this; the ties of affection between him and Professor de Volder, and his great interest in mathematics in this period, also shared by Johan van den Bergh, is well-known . When in 1697 the legacy of Christian Huygens was incorporated in the Library, De Volder was given the task to set this in order; it need not be doubted that Boerhaave was allowed to have a look at these documents, and that he has exchanged ideas with his friend and teacher on the theses in them.

The time spent in the University Library, then, has been extremely fruitful for Boerhaave. Not only did he find there a treasure of wisdom, but also a lifelong friend, who had immediately resolved to 'make the Fortune of the Man by all possible means': Johan van den Bergh. It was on his advice that Boerhaave began to study medicine; the seeds of his subsequent fame have been sown in the Library.

A.M.L.-E.

# 8. PROFESSOR AT THE UNIVERSITY

An appointment at a University entailed that the new Professor was to hold an inaugural oration. This implied that it was only after this inauguration that he could begin to lecture. Such ceremonies took place in the Grand Auditorium, where the community of University members gathered to listen to their new Professor. Ceremonies of commemoration, laudations, solemn and often costly graduation ceremonies, *more majorum* (according to the custom of our ancestors), were also held in the Grand Auditorium. On such occasions this was adorned with flowers and tapestries. The Governors of the University sat on velvet cushions on the bench especially reserved for them, close by the rostrum; the Senate, comprehending all Professors, sat on each side of the hall. The students stood in the middle, behind the benches in front. They were dressed up to the nines, with hats and swords, as can be seen on a print of F. van Bleyswijk, dating from 1715. In the foreground of this representation one sees also the beadles with their staffs, on which the image of Minerva is discernible.

The occasion actually depicted in this print is the oration which was held each year by the Rector of the University; and in this year 1715 it was Boerhaave who held this office. Hence added lustre was given to the event; for by now Boerhaave was deservedly held to be the pride of the University.

Between 1701 and 1738, the years of Boerhaave's teaching, 1919 students were enrolled for medical studies. Approximately a third of them came from English-speaking countries. More than half of his doctoral students – 102, as against 75 Dutchmen – were foreigners. Many of these young doctors were to become prominent physicians in their own countries.

Boerhaave was wont to lecture on botany in the early hours of the morning; afterwards he received patients at home. Later in the day he lectured both *publice* and *privatim*, that is to say, that he gave public lectures in the University building, as well as private ones in his own home. For the latter the students had to pay an additional Hfl. 30,– in each academic year. These private lectures were much frequented. In them theory as well as practical medicine came up for discussion. Subscription lists for the years 1736–'37 and 1737–'38 have been preserved, and show an average audience of a hundred students, with a noticeable number of foreigners among them. We do not know, however, how Professors managed to receive them all in their houses.

How should Boerhaave's teaching be characterised, and where were those lectures given?

HERMANNI BOERHAAVE
SERMO ACADEMICUS
DE COMPARANDO CERTO
IN PHYSICIS.

LUGDUNI BATAVORUM,
Apud PETRUM VANDER Aa, Bibliopolam.

MDCCXV.

23.    The Great Auditorium with Boerhaave holding an oration. Engraving by F. van Bleyswijk (1715).

Boerhaave wished to found medicine on a scientific basis. In his *Institutiones medicae*, a manual on the fundamental tenets of medicine, he emphasises how important it is to regard the body as a mechanical structure, subject to the laws of physics. In another important work, the *Aphorisms on the Diagnosis and Treatment of Diseases*, he showed himself to be a dedicated follower of Hippocrates in his medical views. Boerhaave's therapeutic prescriptions were eagerly noted down by his students. They were even published without his permission; hence in 1719 he felt obliged to publish an authorised version. These books, *De materia medica* (Body of Prescriptions), and *De viribus medicamentorum*. (A Treatise on the Virtue and Energy of Medicines), as well as the *Praelectiones* (published versions of lecture notes) were very popular among students. It was the *Auditorium Medicum*, which was reserved for such theoretical lectures, but it cannot be doubted that Boerhaave, moreover, gave demonstrations of healing herbs in the Botanical Garden, just as he dictated prescriptions when he demonstrated typical cases of various diseases in the Caecilia Hospital.

In 1718 he was appointed in the Chair of Chemistry. He has performed the task of teaching this subject in a dedicated manner. For this he had a laboratory at his disposal, the *Laboratorium Chymicum*, which had been newly fitted up in 1686; previously, the Governors of the University in 1669 had merely allotted a simple little house for this purpose to the first Leiden teacher of chemistry, Carel de Maets (see fig. 24, *sub* Y). The laboratory was a building of 5,5 by 6 metres; regrettably, we know nothing about its layout. It has been demolished in 1819. Furthermore, Boerhaave had some excellent instruments at his disposal: for instance, the hydrostatic balance of 's Gravesande, and the air pump and thermometer of Fahrenheit. Indoubtedly, Boerhaave did carry out experiments in this laboratory; this can be gathered from his manual, *Elementa chemiae*, published in 1732. One of his experiments consisted of producing vinegar in a swift and simple manner; this has been put to industrial use. Boerhaave certainly regarded chemistry as an independent science. In this respect he followed Boyle, whom he greatly admired, and whose meticulous methods of working and cautious judgement served as his model.

The students were fascinated by his demonstrations, in particular when he carried out experiments with biological substances. He demonstrated, for example, the identity of albumen from a hen's egg and the blood serum, and he isolated urea from urine. During all such experiments he kept well away from alchemistic speculations. According to Boerhaave chemistry, like the other sciences, required a positivistic approach; for this view he is remembered with reverence by his successors.                                                                                           A.M.L.-E.

## 9. THE BOTANICAL GARDEN

At first sight it may seem strange that a physician has been the Director of the *Hortus Botanicus* in Leiden, the University's Botanical Garden. Yet when one views this fact in the light of the history of that Garden, it was nothing unusual.

In 1592 the Board of Governors of the University had approached Carolus Clusius for the post of *Praefectus Horti*, (Director of the Botanical Garden); in October 1593 he had actually assumed this office; and from Clusius onwards, until the middle of the 19th century, it has always been a physician who has carried out these duties.

This fact is not really to be wondered at, if one realises that during a long time botany was no independent science; it was subservient to medicine. The major part of each botanical garden was planted with medicinal plants, grown for the cure of patients. Actually, such a garden was more often referred to as *Hortus Medicus*, (Medicinal Garden) than as *Hortus Botanicus*.

From May 9, 1695 to January 10, 1709 it had been Petrus Hotton, who had filled the post of Director of the Garden; when he died a new Professor of Botany had to be appointed. There was only one serious candidate for that Chair, the Swiss scientist Johann Jacob Scheuchzer from Zürich. The Board of Governors, however, were faced with an awkward problem. In 1703 Boerhaave had received an attractive offer of the University of Groningen, but he let it be known that he would prefer to stay in Leiden. Therefore the Governors of the University had promised him the first Chair in the Medical Faculty which would fall vacant; and because it was laid down by statute that no more than four Chairs were to be available in that faculty, Hotton's death was the only possibility for them to keep their promise. Yet Scheuchzer was famous throughout Europe as an expert in botany and natural history – and Boerhaave was not really at home in the field of botany. Even so, it was Boerhaave who was appointed; a fact which caused rather a stir in the scholarly world!

On May 20, 1709 Boerhaave assumed his office, which included the task of the *Praefectus Horti*. His annual salary was immediately raised to Hfl. 1000,– with an extra allowance of Hfl. 300,– for covering the costs of his extensive correspondence.

Boerhaave acquired his knowledge of botany 'from the book,

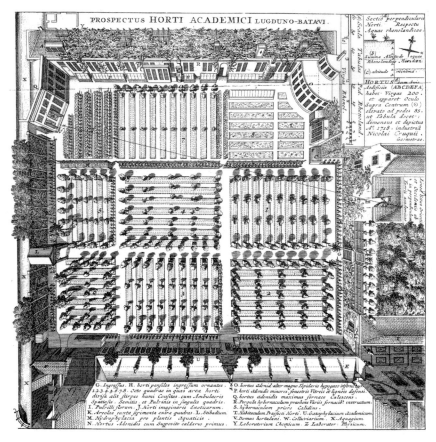

24. Map of the Botanical Garden of the University, an imagined view from a height of 26 m. Below on the right the official residence of the *Praefectus Horti*, at the top to the left the *Laboratorium Chymicum*. Engraving by N. Cruquius (1718).

called *Flora,* of Professor Hermann, although he never himself heard the latter'; this is stated by Schultens in his funeral oration at the burial of Boerhaave in 1739. It evidently means that he had never been among the students attending the lectures of the famous Leiden Professor Paulus Hermann, who had been the Director of the Garden from August 25, 1680 to January 25, 1695. Indubitably, Boerhaave has also gathered his knowledge of botany by studying the collection of living plants in the Garden, as well as dried plants, that is, herbarium material. In his letters Boerhaave writes that he will quickly have to brush up his botanical knowledge; for he took his duties as the Director of the Garden seriously.

It is almost certain that the so-called *Herbarium Boerhaavianum* (the Herbarium of Boerhaave), four volumes of which are preserved in the British Museum of Natural History in London, has not, or only for a very minor part, been collected by Boerhaave himself; he may have used it as a manual. Probably, not even the notes of the labels on the leaves of the herbarium (such labels are characteristic of the period) are in Boerhaave's handwriting. They are, moreover, written by somebody who had only a slight knowledge of botany, for there are many mistakes in the spelling of the botanical names in Latin of the plants – which is something which does not occur in Boerhaave's letters. One finds, for instance, *Abiax* for *Abies*, *Fuschi* instead of *Fuchsi; Zonchus*, which should have been *Sonchus*.

At the end of the volumes 2 and 4 an alphabetic list of contents is included. The way in which the leaves are numbered seems haphazard, for only the right-hand pages are given a number; but this way of numbering is quite common in that period. The most significant fact, however, is that a number of plants in this herbarium is dated in 1665 – which is, then, three years before Boerhaave was born – and it continues up to 1693. Anyway, it was quite usual in this time to possess a herbarium which had been collected by another, and Boerhaave himself also attempted to buy herbaria which were collected by others, as he writes in a letter to William Sherard.

Repeatedly reports circulate, claiming that *the* Boerhaave Herbarium has been found, but alas, up to now these turn out to be no more than idle rumours. Even so, in the State Herbarium in Leiden some genuine herbarium leaves of Boerhaave are preserved, with labels on which he himself has written particulars about those dried plants.

Shortly after Boerhaave had assumed his duties as the *Praefectus Horti*, in 1710, he published a modest catalogue of the plants to be found in the Garden, as was usual in that period. In some of his letters to William Sherard he writes that it gives him a lot of work, because Hotton's heirs do not want to give up any written material to him; indeed, they even claim that there is nothing among the papers left by Hotton, which looks like a catalogue.

In 1720, that is, the year in which Boerhaave's *Index Alter* (Second Catalogue) is dated, he again publishes a catalogue of the plants to be found in the Garden. When this catalogue is carefully scrutinised, it becomes apparent that it is a source of considerable confusion: for it

71

turns out to be exactly the same catalogue as the one written by P. Hermann and printed in 1687 by the publishing house of Cornelis Boutesteyn.

The Boerhaave catalogue in question, printed by Janssonius, has a new title page (even so, without the name of an author) and new preliminary pages, containing a rather detailed historical introduction, in which the name of Hermann does occur, but that of Boerhaave, not. Even so, it becomes evident from the last part of this text that Boerhaave was its author.

It is possible that a considerable number of unpublished copies of Hermann's catalogue had remained with the publisher Boutesteyn, and that somehow they had passed into the hands of Janssonius, but those data are no longer retrievable; yet the fact remains that in both lists of plants on p. 249 the same mistake in numbering occurs, and that the pages of both catalogues are as like as two peas in a pod.

Boerhaave set to work with unbounded energy; this is very evident from the diary of his devoted friend, the Swiss Albrecht von Haller, who stayed in Holland from 1725 to 1727, and during some time was one of Boerhaave's students. He was allowed each day to spend two hours in the Garden, and so he was able daily to observe Boerhaave's activities at first hand. He bears witness to this in his diary, in a detailed and grateful manner. Among other things he confirms that when Boerhaave was appointed in 1709 his knowledge of botany was rather limited, although he was better 'in all other subjects'.

'Yet he applied himself to this with such great seriousness, that after the severe winter of 1709 and no more than two years after his appointment, in 1710, he was able to publish a catalogue of plants, which proves to be richer than all earlier ones; but since then he has himself admitted that this fruit had been somewhat premature and therefore not perfect, as becomes also sufficiently evident when one compares it to the unforgettable work of 1720'.

Obviously, Von Haller was very much impressed by the *Index alter* of 1720, and also by the speed with which Boerhaave was able to bring his botanical knowledge up to a high standard. We are also told in Von Haller's diary that Boerhaave from seven o' clock in the morning onwards was already present in the Garden, together with his students, 'that he pointed out the herbs in the garden; by and large he could each morning enumerate a hundred plants with their many surnames, without needing to look them up.' Oud-Poelgeest, Boerhaave's country estate, is also mentioned in the diary: 'When he could

25. H. Boerhaave, *Index Seminum Satorum* (1717).

tear himself away, he often spent several hours on his vast country estate, where he very carefully raised the plants for which there was no room in the common Garden.'

After a very brief period it became already evident that this Garden was far too small to accommodate the harvest of Boerhaave's strenuous activity in acquiring new plants; he therefore submitted a request to the Governors for being allowed to use the Maliebaan, adjacent to the Botanical Garden, for an expansion. This was granted, and for the time being the problems of space were solved, as far as trees and shrubs were concerned; although he complains that this location is far from ideal. Moreover, in addition to the three greenhouses already in existence (which were provided with a heating system, a novelty dating from 1687), a fourth greenhouse was built, which could also be heated. On the very detailed print of the Garden, made in 1718 by the land surveyor Nicolai Cruquius, one can very clearly discern what it looked like in Boerhaave's time. The first layout of the Garden, dating from 1594, that is, the four squares, are situated in the lower corner on the right of the picture, and to the right the entrance gate is visible; the 17th-century expansions of the Garden and in particular the greenhouses can easily be found in it. Yet even this enlarged Garden soon became too small as well for the steadily increasing collection of plants.

Yet through Boerhaave's purchase of the country seat Oud-Poelgeest in Oegstgeest, already mentioned, he could give free rein to his ambition to raise plants, both for scientific purposes and for pleasure; and he has been able to indulge this hobby to the end of his life to his heart's content (at least in as far as the serious illness which befell him in 1729 allowed for this). Hence he wrote on August 24, 1736 to his former student and friend Bassand, who lived in Vienna: 'There I live with my plants, growing old, yet desiring to acquire even more of them. Amiable, sweet folly! Forget the folly of a friend who grows older, but who still desires to sow trees, – trees which only our grandchildren will see, and which will give their shadow only to them.' Such is the sigh heaved by many a gardener; and it also clearly illustrates that Boerhaave had a special predilection for trees.

The tree which should be especially associated with Boerhaave is not the very well-known Tulip tree (*Liriodendron tulipifera* L.) on Oud-Poelgeest (which, alas, has now died). This tree was planted only in 1785 by one of his descendants. But it was a Manna Ash (*Fraxinus ornus* L.), which Boerhaave himself had grafted on a rootstock of a common Ash (*Fraxinus excelsior* L.), and which is already mentioned in the catalogue of 1710. It is a pity that already in 1845 this tree could not anymore be found in the Botanical Garden; its health had greatly deteriorated and eventually it died. There is a story that Boerhaave was so much impressed by the curative qualities of the Ash, that he always doffed his hat when he passed an Ash; it is not to be wondered at, then, that he himself planted one of them in the Botanical Garden.

Although Boerhaave, according to Haller, almost lived in the *Hortus*, there were also some gardeners; viz., a head gardener (*hortulanus*) and an undergardener. In the *Instruction for the Professor of Botany and the Hortulanus*, dating from 1692 (and in a new, expanded, edition of this, dating from 1723) article I reads: 'That the general direction of the Garden shall be, and remain, absolutely and exclusively under the supervision, care, and guidance of the Professor of Botany, who is to deploy his zeal and diligence to this aim, that via a good correspondence at home and abroad this Garden will become more and more equipped with all Seeds and Plants which will be available, by purchase, barter, or exchange, etc.' This policy is still

74

continued, up to the present. In article III of the same Instruction: 'That he shall also diligently check that all the said Trees, Plants, Seeds, and other Vegetation will be treated, cultivated and propagated with suitable orderliness and care, so that they add to the greater usefulness and glory of the said Garden.' In this respect the Board of Governors of the University has certainly not been disappointed by Boerhaave – quite the contrary! And on the tricky business of *meum* and *tuum* Article IX of the *Instruction of the Hortulanus and the undergardener of the Herb Garden* says: 'They shall not sell, trade in, or give away Trees, Bulbs, Plants, or Herbs, of any kind whatsoever.' For sometimes it happened in this age that the *hortulanus* set up a little trade in living or dried plants, just to line his own purse. Anyway, the policy is nowadays slightly more lenient, even if everything which is sold, exchanged, or given away always, in one way or another, benefits the Garden.

The *hortulanus* appointed in Boerhaave's time was Willem de Hertogh. He died in 1723, and at Boerhaave's request he was succeeded by the undergardener, Jacob Ligtvoet. The latter had been trained by his predecessor, for in that period no other form of horticultural tuition was available. Through this policy a useful continuity was safeguarded, although it also entailed the danger of hidebound rigidity. These two gardeners did quite a lot of work, but Boerhaave himself did his share in the work as well. Each day, and often already at sunrise, he was on his clogs busy in the Garden.

Another and very important part of his duties was the acquisition of plants and seeds, both to keep up the collection and to enlarge it. A large collection imparted the requisite standing to a Botanical Garden, to its Director, and certainly also to a University.

It was in particular the acquisition of seeds which was the most important source of new assets. This was achieved mainly through exchange of letters; hence that addition of Hfl. 300,– to Boerhaave's annual income of Hfl. 1000,–. This enabled him to conduct a wide-flung correspondence, and to defray the costs of sending and receiving parcels.

This extensive correspondence for acquiring vegetable material is very well illustrated by the three volumes of his *Index seminum satorum* (List of Sown Seeds). This 'diary of the exchange of seeds', written by his own hand, covers the period from 1712 to 1727. All kinds of details are to be found in it about his connections with more than 50 botanists, general contacts, for instance in the V.O.C. (the United East India Company), and scientists at home and abroad. Via the ships of the V.O.C. very many unknown tropical and subtropical plants and seeds were imported in our country. Not all of these were destined for the Botanical Garden in Leiden, however; a part of them ended up in the *Hortus* of the rich mercantile town of Amsterdam (a fierce competition and rivalry between the two Botanical Gardens had already been going on for a long time), as well as in a number of private gardens of merchants; some of them had contacts, either immediately or via relations and friends, in the V.O.C., or in the East Indies, or elsewhere in the world. Boerhaave received many consignments of plants and seeds and he was in his turn very generous with regard to the sending of interesting specimens of vegetation to others.

To mention only a few of Boerhaave's contacts:

- *Simon van Beaumont,* the Clerk of the States-General mediated between him and the V.O.C. for the acquisition of plants; and Angelo van Gezel, ship's surgeon of the V.O.C. in Ceylon, sent not only plants but also fishes, birds, and insects for the 'museum'.
- *Josua Boerhaave,* a relation, who was a trader on the Gold Coast, in 1715 forwarded vegetables (seeds) with the ship 'Guntersteyn'.
- *Caspar Commelin,* Professor in Amsterdam and Director of the Botanical Garden there, sent seeds from Curaçao, Bengal, and Africa.
- *Francesco Cupani,* Director of the *Hortus Catholicus* in Palermo, was one of Boerhaave's correspondents; likewise P.A. Micheli, a famous botanist and Director of the Botanical Garden in Florence.
- Boerhaave corresponded very frequently with *William Sherard,* the English consul in Smyrna, who sent him seeds from West India, North- and South Carolina (in America), and also seeds from the Near and Far East.
- *Sir Hans Sloane,* who set up the Chelsea Physic Garden in London, and was the founder of the English Society of Apothecaries, forwarded seeds of plants in America and Ceylon to Boerhaave, who in his turn sent a collection of rare plants from the Leiden *Hortus* to the garden of Sloane.

The list could be extended at will, for in the *Index seminum satorum* 17 Dutchmen are mentioned – for the most part living in overseas territories – as well as 10 Italians, 9 Germans, 8 Englishmen, 5 Frenchmen, 2 Spaniards, and one Swiss.

It may be easily imagined that the collection of the Leiden *Hortus* became enormously extensive, and it is not to be wondered at that very soon Boerhaave considered the grounds of the Garden and the Maliebaan, in use for the cultivation of trees, to be too small.

The purchase of Oud-Poelgeest, then, provided him eventually with the space required for cultivation; and it becomes apparent from the notes he made in 1725 on the sowing of seeds, *tam in horto Academiae, quam in villa mea*, (both in the garden of the University and in my country seat), that he actually used its garden for this purpose. The important role of Oud-Poelgeest as a space for the Botanical Garden's overflow is even more clearly illustrated by the sudden decline in the numbers of plants after Boerhaave's death: in 1720 the species of plants grown numbered 5846 (and the number of varieties grown came up to more than 7000!), but in 1740, that is, a mere two years after Boerhaave's death in 1738, the number of plant species in the collection of the *Hortus* in Leiden had suddenly sunk to 3016 (and the number of varieties to only slightly more than 3500 specimens).

Regrettably, no catalogue or counts are known of the number of plants grown, shortly after Boerhaave bought Oud-Poelgeest; it would have been very interesting to see how quickly he had amassed his vast collection, and it would not really surprise us if the collection of Oud-Poelgeest would have surpassed that of the Botanical Garden in the town as to numbers. Two causes can be pointed out for the sharp decrease of the latter after Boerhaave's death: firstly, between 1720 and 1740 no catalogue has been published, and so no counts can be made; and secondly, the plants in the garden of Oud-Poelgeest probably have remained there when Boerhaave resigned his offices of *Horti Praefectus* and Professor of Botany. The Board of Governors of the University accepted his resignation only reluctantly. He was succeeded by the lecturer Adriaen van Royen; it was he who published the catalogue of 1740, which plays such an important role in our countings.

It is evident, then, that the influence of Boerhaave on the *Hortus* in Leiden and its collection of plants has been great; and the question could be raised whether this does also apply to botany in general. According to F.W.T. Hunger, Boerhaave 'has not been a reformer in the field of botany, who has pointed out new ways for this science through brilliant discoveries or new theories; his importance as a botanist is mainly determined by the indefatigable care he gave to the Garden of the University of Leiden, and by a publication of a list of names of plants to be found in it.' To this one should certainly add the influence exerted by Boerhaave on his contemporaries and students, both in his immediate contacts and in the extensive and frequent correspondence he carried on with many scientists, old students, and friends.

His influence in the science of botany is perhaps most clearly to be discerned in his *Index alter*, published in 1720, and comprehending more than 5800 plants. Like many of his predecessors, contemporaries, and successors, Boerhaave was very much interested in a good system of naming and registering plants. It was, after all, an age in which many journeys were made to newly discovered territories both in the East and in the West, and many new plants of kinds still unknown came to Europe.

The current descriptive manner of naming plants, the so-called paraphrasing nomenclature in the long run turned out to be inadequate for coping with all such novelties. Renowned botanists like Bauhin and Tournefort were at work to devise a new system which would preferably be more simple and clear. Boerhaave also contributed something to this – that can be clearly seen in the *Index alter*. Yet he was very deeply aware of the fact that he was not the man who would achieve this aim; for in the Preface to the *Index alter* he himself writes: 'I know that as yet I am not capable of constructing a neatly fitting system, indeed, that I will never be able to accomplish this, even if I would reach the age of Methuselah and devote myself wholly to this task.'

Yet he has been well acquainted with the man who actually managed to accomplish this work: Carolus Linnaeus from Sweden, who in 1735 travelled to Holland. Among his luggage he had a number of manuscripts, for which he hoped to find a publisher in our country. One of these manuscripts, the little book called *Systema naturae*, which nowadays has become exceedingly rare, was, as it were, the blueprint or forerunner of the systematic classification of nature, his life's work, the *Species plantarum* of 1753. Linnaeus also wanted to visit the Botanical Gardens in Amsterdam and Leiden. A visit to the famous Boerhaave was also one of his dearest wishes, and after some initial difficulties Linnaeus became acquainted with Boerhaave, and visited both the house of the latter in Leiden, which was adjacent to the Garden, and Oud-Poelgeest. He was very much impressed by the collection of trees planted there. This acquaintance went beyond a single meeting. Linnaeus has learned much from Boerhaave, and with regard to the collection of plants in the *Hortus* he said 'that simply and solely through Boerhaave's care the number has increased so much that no other Botanical Garden in Europe has ever comprehended so many specimens'.

Although in Boerhaave's time the distinction between species of plants was still a matter of great confusion and plants could have various names – it all depended on which description by some famous botanist one preferred to adopt – the work of Boerhaave contributed something to a clearer system. To mention only one example: the water violet, belonging to the family of *Primulaceae*, was a water plant which in that period grew more commonly in the (still clean) ditches than is the case now, when ditches are often polluted. Before Boerhaave gave his attention to the nomenclature of this beautiful plant, it had various Latin names, for instance, *Millefolium aquaticum; Viola aquatica, caule nudo; Myriophyllum, equisetifolium, fluviatile*; all of which is very confusing. In Boerhaave's *Index alter* it becomes evident that he has named the plant after his predecessor Paulus Hotton: '*Hottonia palustris* ', and when we look in Linnaeus' *Species plantarum* of 1735, we see that he has adopted the name given by Boerhaave, with a first reference to Boerhaave's work: '*Hottonia palustris* Boerh. lugdb. 1. 207'. This is proof of the respect that the student Linnaeus felt for his teacher Boerhaave! It may be added that 'Hottonia palustris' is the name still in use up to the present day for this beautiful plant which, alas, has become very rare.          M.C.C.T.

## 10. THE OFFICIAL RESIDENCE IN THE NONNENSTEEG

In 1594, when the layout of the Botanical Garden had been completed, the Governors of the University made some arrangements to ensure the smooth running of things. One of their main concerns was an adequate surveillance. Two officials were responsible for maintaining the requisite order, viz., the Professor of Medicine who was especially entrusted with the teaching of botany, and the actual caretaker of the garden, usually called the *hortulanus*. The first *hortulanus* was Dirc Outgaertsz. Cluyt, and in 1595 the house of the second beadle on the Achtergracht (now: Doelengracht) was allotted to him. The back of this house was adjacent to, and overlooked the Garden, and so a continual surveillance was ensured. But something was found for the Professor as well: in the Nonnensteeg, and immediately adjoining the University building, stood the house of the first beadle. In 1598 this was allotted to the Professor of Botany, and it has remained the official residence of the *Praefectus Horti*, the Director of the Botanical Garden, until far into the nineteenth century.

After Boerhaave's appointment it was a matter of course that this new Professor of Botany would move into the official residence. In this period it was customary to move house either on May 1, or on November the first. Around those dates the bustle in the streets was noticeable: everywhere one saw boats and carts full of household goods on their way to another house. Hence there was each year a peak of weddings in April and the beginning of May and, to a lesser extent, in October. Now although the house in the Nonnensteeg, being an official residence, was not subject to this ironclad law, Boerhaave probably will not have taken possession of it before the first of May. After all, he had to leave his previous home, and new inhabitants of that could only on the first of May move into it. And although he was unmarried, it is not impossible that he gave house-room to one or several of his (half)brothers or -sisters. A domestic staff was indispensable, even if he may have taken over one of more of Hotton's servants; there may have been student boarders too. Summarising, then, one can think of many reasons why Herman did not trudge along with his furniture and books in the dead of winter, but calmly awaited the appropriate time about May the first. Moreover, Boerhaave had to wait for the very large library of Hotton to be removed before there was room for his own books; and that library was auctioned only on May 22, 1709.

26.   The Lecturer Boerhaave. Engraving by J. Folkema, from Boerhaave, *Over de kragten der Geneesmiddelen* (1756).

It is virtually certain, however, that those books were not placed in the official residence itself. From 1599 onwards a gallery was to be found on the southern side of the Botanical Garden in which delicate plants could winter: the so-called *ambulacrum*. At one corner this adjoined the Professor's residence; a little porch connected the two. Therefore the Professor could enter the Garden through the house, via the *ambulacrum*. In the course of time, however, this had become more or less supererogatory for wintering plants, mainly because new greenhouses had been built on more suitable locations. Of old this gallery also provided accommodation for a large collection of stuffed animals, dried plants, minerals, medicines, and even pictures and objects from distant countries, mainly the East and West Indies. Such objects were used for the teaching of students of medicine; they were a forerunner of the Museum of Natural History. The management of this collection was entrusted to the Professor of Anatomy. The curiosities on display here greatly impressed many visitors, witness the fact that the contents of the 'collection of curiosities' or 'gallery of beasts' are often mentioned in travel books. From this *ambulacrum*, then, a part had been partitioned off to serve as a library and lecture room for the Professor of Botany. Evidently, the remaining part was sufficiently large to house the collection, which had somewhat deteriorated. Here as well as in the Anatomical Theatre it was put on record in 1719 that 'owing to the long passage of time the greater part of the curiosities had very much decayed'. Therefore the merchant ships trading on the East and West Indies were appealed to 'to convey hither all kinds of curiosities'. The question remains whether the administrator at that time has exerted himself to replace the exotics. We know nothing about Boerhaave's policy in this respect.

It was also in Boerhaave's interest, then, that in 1727 the roof of the *ambulacrum* was renovated. It cannot be discerned now whether the immediate cause for this was mere old age or storm damage; but we do know that the old wooden roof was replaced by top quality blue glazed tiles. Moreover, the number of dormer windows was reduced from twelve to six.

This was only one of Boerhaave's building activities in the Garden, however. More important was the building, immediately after his appointment, of a greenhouse, 9,5 metres long but rather shallow, against the wall along the Achtergracht. This greenhouse had a curiously sloping roof, devised to catch as much of the sunshine as possible, for actually the location was not ideal for a greenhouse.

27. The *Theatrum Physicum* ; to the right the official residence of the Professor of Botany. Coloured drawing by J.J. Bijlaert (ca. 1770).

When the Hortus was again enlarged in 1736, under the direction of Boerhaave's successor Van Royen, it was again demolished – Boerhaave lived to see this – because it blocked the passage. It was to be replaced by the Orangery, which was far larger.

No changes have been made in the official residence itself during the time Boerhaave lived there. The back of the house, which is known from the bird's eye view drawn by Cruquius in 1718, remained unchanged until 1772, when the entire house received a facelift. It is a pity that no good representation can be found of the front of the official residence in the Nonnensteeg, but various data warrant the conclusion that it was a considerable property with sufficient room for a family of moderate size, like that of Boerhaave.

He married rather soon after he had moved into the house in the Nonnensteeg. With their children and some domestics the Boerhaaves may well have lived comfortably there. The children probably have been born in it as well: the first was Johanna Maria, baptised on March 20, 1712 in the Hooglandse kerk (baptisms commonly took place in this church), with the proud grandfather Abraham Drolen vaux and the great-grandmother Jeanne de Pire, surely as proud, as godparents; then Maghdalena, baptised on May 7, 1713 in the Hooglandse kerk with the Rev. Jacobus Boerhave and Maghdalena Boerhave as her godparents; and finally Maghdalena Jacoba, baptised on May 30, 1714; the ceremony this time took place in the Pieterskerk (a baptism here was more distinguished), with the same godparents, the Rev. Jacobus Boerhave 'minister in this town' – and Maghdalena Boerhave. Boerhaave lost his two youngest children when they were still very young; it cannot but have deeply affected him as a physician, that he was unable to preserve their lives. This must have been felt still more sharply with the child which was born on June 9, 1721, but died already after two days, even before it had been possible to baptise it.

During the time Boerhaave lived in the official residence he has received various important guests. Indubitably, the visit which most impressed the inhabitants of Leiden was that of Peter the Great, Czar of Russia. He visited Boerhaave in 1715, arriving on his yacht, which moored in the Rapenburg, and before he went to see the Anatomical Theatre.

Boerhaave received the Czar, according to the wish of the latter, at 5 o'clock in the morning. Peter showed great interest in the Botanical Garden and the way in which plants were registered; but during the conversation, which lasted two hours, he also asked many searching questions about medicine. In the same year his great interest in medicine, in particular in anatomy, led to his purchase of the collections of the Amsterdam anatomist Frederik Ruysch. Boerhaave often visited Ruysch; a long-standing friendship joined him with the anatomist, and he was fully conversant with the contents of the collection of Ruysch. Hence it was Boerhaave who in 1717 was to arrange the valuable collections to be sent to Russia. It is quite possible that Peter has discussed them with Boerhaave.                    P.J.M.d.B./H.B.

# 11. THE CAECILIA HOSPITAL AND CLINICAL TEACHING

On Saturday September 21, 1737 students hastened to the Caecilia Hospital. For more than a century, from 1636 onwards, clinical teaching had been given here; during several years, however, no patients had been available for this purpose. But now there were again some patients, who would be demonstrated by Boerhaave, by now sixty-nine years old, with the assistance of the town physicians and surgeons. From the galleries above the box beds students tried to follow the lessons of their teacher. The Professor examined the patients in their box beds, and explained the details of the diseases and the way in which they ought to be treated to the students. Finally, he prescribed the necessary remedies; these were written down in the book of prescriptions, so as to enable the students to copy the prescriptions of their famous teacher, and in the future to use them themselves for their patients. Usually, the students showed more

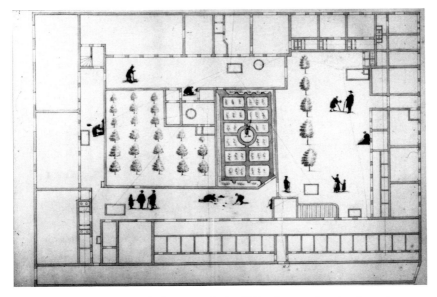

28.  The Caecilia Hospital. Copy made in 1860 of an undated coloured drawing of its ground plan.

interest in those prescriptions than in the actual demonstration. At times the Professor called upon an advanced student to examine the patient; he was to give his opinion of the case, and to prescribe the necessary remedies. When the visit to the patients had come to an end, the Professor and his audience went to see the 'binnenvader' and 'binnenmoeder' (the couple who were entrusted with the management and care for the hospital's inmates), in order to indicate what kinds of food and drink must be given to the patients.

In this way the Caecilia Hospital contributed to the 'constant care for the destitute Patients' and, moreover, it was of 'incredible and invaluable benefit for the inquisitive young people, who apply themselves zealously ... to acquire a thorough knowledge of Medicine'.

To begin with, after the siege and relief of Leiden, the Caecilia Hospital was used as a kind of annexe of the Catharina Hospital,

*Vüe de la Maison des Insensés se regardant par derriere.* | *Gesigt van het Dol-huys op de binnen plaats.*

29.  The inner court of the Caecilia Hospital. Engraving by A. Rademaker (1732)

housing plague patients, raving madmen, and also *proveniers* – people who bought themselves into the hospital, which provided them with bed and board. The Professors of Medicine had advised to convert what had previously been the Convent of St. Caecilia in the Camp into a hospital (fig. 28).; and a lottery held in 1596 had yielded sufficient funds for this plan. The *proveniers* were housed in an 'Upper-Storey Hall for Men', and the women among them in another one – each provided with 21 box beds; these halls were situated on the side of the Vrouwencamp (now: Caeciliastraat). On the same side of the building was also the room of the Governors. It had a beautiful entrance, decorated with armorial bearings. Smaller halls for *proveniers* were situated on the side of the Josephsteeg (now: Zionsteeg). Some ten little houses, again for *proveniers*, were built on the side of the Vrouwenkerkkoorsteeg and the Vrouwencamp. The hospital proper for the plague-patients and madmen was built on the side of the Dolhuisgracht, with on the ground floor twenty cells for the raving mad; on the first storey were the wards for plague patients, which afterwards were to become the 'wards for patients'. These could be reached along an open stairway outdoors. In front of the entrance to both halls was a large porch with benches; here convalescent patients could enjoy a view of the garden (fig. 29). The box beds in the halls on the upper storey were equipped with galleries on which clothes and bedding could be aired.

When the clinical teaching, the so-called *Collegium Medico-practicum*, was introduced, some changes were made. In the 'wards for the sick' now twelve marked box beds were kept free, six in the men's ward and six in that for women. Moreover, one of the little houses for *proveniers*, on the left side of the gate giving on to the Vrouwenkerkkoorsteeg, was reserved for performing autopsies on patients who had died. An agreement had been arrived at between the Governors of the University and the Burgomasters of Leiden, that when one of the town physicians came upon a 'special kind of disease' in his area, he could see to it that the patient was admitted in the Hospital; such patients, then, were available as subjects for clinical teaching. The patients in question were mainly people who 'because of their poverty were unable to pay for anything, and so must needs be succoured at the expense of the Public'. That was why the Hospital assumed the responsibility for the expenses of nursing and medicines. For all this the Hospital received a compensation of Hfl. 120,– a year from the University.

The clinical teaching greatly prospered, especially under Boer-

D E Burgermeefteren ende Regeerders der Stad Leyden,

hebben goedgevonden by defen, Dat *Grietje Markx*

*weuw van Johannes Angil* fal werden
*Zieleggende uith Vrouwekamp*
ingenomen in een van de twaelf Bedfteden in de *Vrouwe*

Siecke-Zaal in het Cecilien Cafthuys. Des ten oir-
konden defen door laft van de Burgermeefters ende Regeerders voornoemt, onderteyckent op den *10 Sept. 1737*

By my

*Royen*

*Aan d Ed Groot Agtb Heeren*
*Word met eerbiedigheid verzogt, dat de Perfoon van*
*Grietie Markx, Huijsvrouw van Johannes Angil,*
*wonende in de Vrouwe-kamp op den hoek van de*
*Moer anne-fteeg, als zijnde een bequaam Subject*
*ten drenfte van 't Collegium Medico Practicum*
*in het Cecilia Gafthuijs, mag worden geplaatst*
*t welk doende &c. J d Water 1737. 17. 7b.*

*fiat 18 Sept 1737.*

30.    Notes of admittance into the Hospital for Grietje Markx (1737).

90

haave's predecessors, Franciscus de le Boë, Sylvius, Lucas Schacht, and Frederik Dekkers. When it was set up it was still thought to be sufficient that the Professor visited the patients twice a week, on Wednesday and Saturday. Sylvius introduced the daily visit. There were always two Professors who were responsible for giving the *Collegium Medico-practicum*, taking turns at it.

On August 8, 1714 Herman Boerhaave succeeded the Professor Govert Bidloo as a teacher of the *Collegium Medico-practicum*. For this he received an allowance of Hfl. 200,– a year. To begin with, he shared this duty with his older colleague Frederik Dekkers. Because of his old age Dekkers was succeeded in September 1719 by Herman Oosterdijk Schacht. The latter was a man who was fully conversant with the situation in Leiden: in 1693 he had set up a practice as a physician; two years later he was appointed town physician.

Apart from the plague victims, for whom in 1653 a separate hospital had been set up, the Caecilia Hospital in Boerhaave's time had still the same kinds of inmates as in the beginning. *Proveniers* still lived in the halls and houses allotted to them. The cells still served for the 'care and necessary confinement of the raving mad, and all kinds of insane persons'. Apart from them, in these cells people were put 'who overindulge in drunkenness, or any other unseemly way of life, squandering their estates, neglecting their livelihood, to the greatest possible grief of their next of kin, to such an extent that it is fully

31. Diagram showing the number of patients admitted into the Caecilia Hospital in Boerhaave's time.

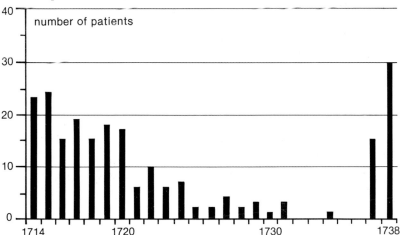

justified to rate them among the insane'. Poor people with a chronic disease could be admitted to the wards of the sick at the expense of the town. In the room of the *Collegium Medico-practicum* autopsies still continued to be performed. The town surgeon and obstetrician of Leiden, Jacob Denijs, narrated how in 1718 Boerhaave in the Hospital and in the presence of numerous students dissected the 'wholly emaciated body' of a woman who had suffered from a 'tumour in the Ovary'.

A few days before Boerhaave recommenced his clinical teaching in 1737, two people had been admitted to the 'box beds of the sick' of the Hospital: Grietje Markx and Kors van der Boon. Grietje, the wife of Johannes Aangel, lived in the immediate neighbourhood of the Hospital, in the Vrouwencamp at the corner of the Moerannesteeg. She suffered from dropsy. The town physician Johannes de Water judged her to be a 'suitable subject for the use of the *Collegium Medico-Practicum*", and asked the Burgomasters of Leiden for the patient to be admitted in the Caecilia Hospital. In a note signed by the Secretary Van Royen he agreed to the hospitalisation 'in one of the twelve bed boxes in the Women's Ward in the Caecilia Hospital' (fig. 30). Hence, on September 18, she was inscribed on the 'List of sick people who have been granted permission to be admitted in the Caecilia Hospital'. On the same day Kors van der Boon, living in the Paradijspoort in the Bouwelouwesteeg, was hospitalised.

This 'List of sick people' shows that during the period that Boerhaave acted as Professor of Clinical Medicine (1714–1738) in total 223 destitute patients were admitted for the purposes of clinical teaching. Most of them lived in the quarters of the town where dire poverty prevailed – in streets like the Looijerstraat, Langegracht, Kaarsenmakerstraat, de Zuidzijde, Meutjesteeg, Mirakelsteeg, Crommelleboogsteeg, de Geregracht, and Uiterstegracht, which were to be found around the centre of the city; many of them are still extant. The address of many was in a 'gate' – an airless, narrow, blind alley with numerous small and poor houses.

The number of patients available to Boerhaave for his teaching fluctuated rather strongly (fig. 31). In the years from 1714 up to and including 1720 an average of 19 patients a year was admitted. Afterwards the number gradually diminished: in the period from 1726 to 1731 no more than one or two patients were hospitalised in each year. The schedule of lectures shows that from 1724 on the *Collegium*

*Medico-practicum* was no longer a daily lecture, but was given only on Wednesdays and Saturdays. After 1731 there was no patient at all available for clinical teaching, with the exception of a single case in 1734. In 1737 the revival set in: in that year 15 destitute patients were admitted, and in the next year as much as 30 cases.

It is evident that in the 1720s Boerhaave had lost some of his interest in clinical teaching. That becomes also apparent in his correspondence with his former student Joannes Baptista Bassand. In September 1726, for instance, Boerhaave wrote that three years earlier he had retired from the 'worrisome practise'. Two years later Bassand asked for information on this point on behalf of one of his protégés, and Boerhaave answered that already for a long time he did not anymore visit patients, a few friends excepted; he was therefore unable to provide Bassand's protégé with clinical training. Indoubtedly, the diseases from which Boerhaave suffered in these years have played an important role here. From July 1722 on he was seriously ill for almost an entire year; five years later it was an 'autumn sickness' which sapped his strength.

32.  The Caecilia Hospital with the staircase giving on to the wards on the first storey. Photograph by J. Lens (1989).

Only a few patients are known in this period: for instance, the 30-year old Sara Kouwe, and Grietje Brand, fifty years old. They have both been observed in 1726 by Albrecht von Haller during his period of study in Leiden, at the demonstration given by Boerhaave. Their names have been preserved because Haller incorporated their case histories in one of his writings.

In February 1738, in a letter to Bassand, Boerhaave expressed his joy that it was again possible for students to accompany him, now that for five months he had again been treating patients in the Hospital. From September 1737 onwards, for reasons as yet unknown, patients were again available for clinical teaching.

The course of lectures given in 1737–1738 became very well-known; primarily because Boerhaave gave his *Introduction to Clinical Practice*, which was to become famous. Two years after his death this *Introductio in Praxin Clinicam* was published for the first time by the Leiden printer Philip Bonk. In this Introduction Boerhaave expounded the principles of clinical examination.

We are fully informed about this course, thanks to the stenographic account of Boerhaave's student Gerard van Swieten. From September 20, 1737 to April 16 1738 he took down minutes both of Boerhaave's introductory lecture, mentioned just now, and of his clinical demonstrations. One of the first patients named by him was Grietje Markx, already mentioned in the above; in total she was shown nine times. She died on November 3, 1737; the day before Boerhaave had still demonstrated her to the students. Two patients in this course afterwards became very famous, albeit not under their own name; but, as they are also referred to in the notes of Van Swieten, by giving their age and disease: a 'sixty-six years old cachectic' (a case of emaciation) and a 'paralytic of sixty-one years'. Afterwards their case histories were incorporated in a collection of Boerhaave's written consultations. The 'cachectic of sixty-six years' may well have been Kors van der Boon, dyer, who lived in the Langebrug, and who was, together with Grietje Markx the first patient to be admitted in the Caecilia Hospital in September 1737. Van der Boon also died in the Hospital, on December 8, 1737.

In the beginning of 1738 Boerhaave became ill. The first symptoms of a lung complaint became manifest. Yet, notwithstanding a growing shortness of breath he continued his lectures in the Caecilia Hospital, as opposed to his other lectures which he terminated in March of that year. On April 16, 1738 Boerhaave still demonstrated

94

four patients, but his heart condition prevented him from finishing his clinical lecture. This was Boerhaave's final lecture; he died a few months afterwards.

The building where Boerhaave has taught to the very end now, through a coincidence, bears his name. The halls, in which *proveniers* and destitute patients were housed, now provide accommodation for the Museum Boerhaave, the National Museum of the History of Science and Medicine. The new destination of the Caecilia Hospital also implies that one now enters the ancient block of buildings through the former storehouse for peat for the Roman Catholic poor, and not, as the students in the past, through the little gate in the Vrouwenkerkkoorsteeg.                    H.B./R.R.

33.   The Weighhouse. Photograph by J. Lens (1986).

## 12. THE WEIGHHOUSE AND THE SURGEONS' CHAMBER

Among the many offices held by Boerhaave was the chairmanship of the Guild of surgeons. From 1604 onwards it had always been a Professor of Medicine who had been appointed as the 'president of the examinators'; and on November 9, 1720 Boerhaave succeeded his colleague Frederik Dekkers in this office. Since then, around two o'clock on each first Wednesday of the month Boerhaave regularly climbed the simple spiral staircase which gave on to the Chamber of the Guild of Surgeons in the Weighhouse. There he chaired the meeting of the *Collegium Chirurgicum* (Board of Surgeons), which examined candidates for the membership of the guild. Apart from the chairman, the *Collegium Chirurgicum* consisted of two doctors of medicine, the Master of the Guild, and two 'examinators'. Their names were displayed on parchment lists of names which embellished the Guild's chamber (and which are still on view in the Museum de Lakenhal).

A Guild of surgeons had existed in the town of Leiden already in the sixteenth century; but it was only on May 4, 1669 that the town council gave permission to this Guild to meet in a room above the Weighhouse. Unlike their Amsterdam colleagues, the surgeons in Leiden were not given their own anatomical theatre. They were allowed, however, to be present at University dissections, both in the Anatomical Theatre in the church of the Begijnhof and in the Caecilia Hospital.

The Weighhouse had been built in 1657 after a design of the well-known architect Pieter Post. It was meant to be an impressive building; that was why a second storey was planned. Maybe, when the building was put up, it was thought that this would be used by the master of the Weighhouse, but in practice it became evident that for him the two little rooms between the weighing-room and the adjacent Boterhal (where the quality of butter was inspected) were adequate. The upper storey was sufficiently large for a meeting room of a medium-sized guild, and so in 1669 this was allotted to the surgeons. The presence of the Guild was announced by means of a wooden sign on the front of the Weighhouse, which read in golden letters: *Collegium Chirurgicum*.

The accommodation for the surgeons consisted of a landing, a large hall, and a smaller room. In the latter the servant of the Guild was housed. Probably, dissections were also performed here. The large hall was, of course, reserved for the *Collegium Chirurgicum*. Its members assembled around the large oval table, sitting on 6 Spanish chairs of walnut; the president had a special armchair, and the previous Master and Deans of the Guild had to be satisfied with a bench. During two days in the month of December a 'merry feast' was organised in this hall, at 'about half-past one', which was paid for from the fines imposed on 'quacks' and 'unqualified barber-surgeons'. The great hall was embellished with pictures, skeletons, and curiosities – part of the latter were on view in a cabinet which was adorned with two horns of rhinoceroses. On the mantelpiece hung a painting made by Jacobus van der Sluys, depicting the Good Samaritan – an allegory of surgery. An imposing cabinet for instruments, dating from 1679, stood facing the chimney. On this cabinet, containing surgical instruments, the painter Jan de Vos had depicted the arms of the Deans of the Guild. The chest of the Guild, in which the archive and the seals were kept, probably stood under this cabinet. The room on the upper storey of the Weighhouse has been in the care of the Guild until 1807. In that year a Board of Medical Inspection was set up, which was again abolished in 1865. From 1869 onwards the furnishings were gradually transferred to the Museum de Lakenhal.

Boerhaave was on friendly terms with several surgeons. The town surgeon, lithotomist, and obstetrician Jacobus Denys enjoyed his special protection. It was in particular Denys's obstetric work of which Boerhaave had a high opinion; hence he saw to it that the town council appointed Denys to teach the midwives their craft. When the court physician in Vienna, Bassand, asked Boerhaave to name a skilful teacher of obstetrics for one of his students who had come to Leiden, it was Denys who was recommended by Boerhaave. Yet Denys was characterised by colleagues as being 'shrewd, pushing, and avaricious'; and at times he lacked courtesy in his dealings with his patron. At one time, for instance, both men were consulted by a patient with a serious complaint of the bladder. Denys diagnosed a stone in the bladder, and wanted to operate; Boerhaave rejected the idea. The patient died a few days later. At the autopsy Denys found a stone the size of an egg; he blamed Boerhaave for the death and maintained that the patient could have been cured if he had been allowed to operate him. But alas for Denys, after a further examination it became evident that the real cause of the disease must be sought in the kidneys, – as has been predicted by Boerhaave. In this way (according to Boerhaave's student Haller) the reputation of a great man was safeguarded.

Denys was several times a member of the *Collegium Chirurgicum* in the role of examinator; in 1724 he even became its Master.

The Guild's archives show that Boerhaave regularly attended the meetings of the *Collegium Chirurgicum,* apart from his periods of illness. Notwithstanding a heart condition which became more and more serious, Boerhaave still chaired the meeting of the *Collegium* on April 2, 1738. A month earlier he had given his last public lecture, and the meeting of April was to be the last one at which Boerhaave would be present. After several months of the president's absence, Bernhard Siegfried Albinus succeeded his deceased teacher on October 1, 1738.

P J.M.d.B./H.B.

99

In 1722 Boerhaave suffered from a rheumatic complaint lasting for several months. His recovery was slow, and he continued to feel a shadow of his old self. The illness had left its mark. Hence he decided to take things somewhat easier, but the claims of his patients and students made this impossible. In a letter to his friend Bassand he sighed: 'Oh, would God that it was granted to me to enjoy the reposeful silence of the country, far from all day-to-day worries!' Maybe this longing for a life in the country of the kind he had known in his youth was at the bottom of Boerhaave's decision to be on the look-out for a country house. There was, however, yet another matter which weighed heavily on him. Repeatedly he had pointed out that the Botanical Garden in Leiden was too small. Moreover, there was also the threat of competition: the Botanical Garden in Utrecht would probably be enlarged. That is why Boerhaave was also seeking room

La Maison de Vieu Poelgeest appartenant à MONS.ʳ 't Huys Oud Poelgeest toebehorende den HEER HER- HERMANUS BOERHAVE Professeur en Medicine. MANUS BOERHAVE Professor in de Medicine.

34.   The manor Oud-Poelgeest. Engraving by A. Rademaker (1732).

for a large garden. In this situation the opportunity arose in 1724 to buy Oud-Poelgeest, or, as Boerhaave described it in his account book: 'the manor Poelgeest, also called Alkemade, with buildings, waterways, and fields'.

The history of Oud-Poelgeest goes far back. In the Middle Ages it was continually in the possession of members of the family Van Alkemade, originating from the castle Oud Alkemade, just outside Warmond. Oud-Poelgeest shared in the fate of many castles and fortified houses in the neighbourhood of Leiden: it was destroyed in the first years of the revolt against Philip II. As was the case with most of these demolished castles, a long time passed before it was planned to rebuild Oud-Poelgeest; and it was only in 1661 that the town council of Leiden granted permission to the owner at that time, Constantin Sohier de Vermandois, to rebuild the manor. This permission was required because the distance between the ruin and the town was less than 800 roods, whereas for military and economical purposes a large area around the town had to be left vacant.

There are some uncertainties with regard to the actual rebuilding. It has been argued that it was only in 1668 that this was done, by the Haarlem architect Erasmus Gerritsz. den Otter, by order of Constantin's daughter Maria Cathérine. In 1691 Oud-Poelgeest became the property of Constantin's great-granddaughter Adriana Constantina. This 'Lady of Warmenhuizen' lived in great style in The Hague. Oud-Poelgeest will not have mattered much to her, for she also possessed the manor of Santvliet in the close vicinity of Lisse. That is why she sold on August 21, 1724 Oud-Poelgeest with grounds of 5 morgen and 286 roods to Boerhaave for Hfl. 8923,–. In any case Lady Adriana did not yet sell the entire property around Oud-Poelgeest; a manor or castle was often a financial burden because it had to be kept in repair, but parcels of arable land and meadows usually were a good investment. Gradually, however, Boerhaave managed to gain possession of the other parcels of land; and so he became a large landowner in this part of Oegstgeest.

The manor was situated close to the Haarlemmertrekvaart, on the spot where the towing-barge must draw to a stop in order to let the horse cross the bridge of the Kwaak. This will have been convenient for Boerhaave: during this stop there was time to hand in a letter, or for somebody to get on board or leave the barge. Each day about ten towing-barges went to Leiden or Haarlem.

In Oud-Poelgeest Boerhaave would be able to receive his guests in a suitable manner. For this purpose the house was done up. For

35.   The manor Oud-Poelgeest ( the rear). Photograph by J. Lens (1986).

instance, he bought from a house on the Oude Singel, which was being altered, for Hfl. 207,– a painted wallpaper for Oud-Poelgeest.

But, of course, it was especially the large garden which had attracted Boerhaave, He wrote enthusiastically to the botanist William Sherard, an old friend, that he had bought a garden which was 24 times as large as the Garden of the University. Regrettably, however, everything had still to be planted. Boerhaave's account book shows that in 1724 he spent Hfl.300,– on trees, and Hfl. 41,– on 'garden implements'. In the following years there are also recurrent entries for purchasing trees and shrubs. It goes without saying that friends regularly sent him seeds and plants. Especially his friend Bassand was an important contributor; hence Boerhaave wrote in one of his letters: 'My Botanical Garden, proudly displaying its Bassandian gifts, shows your liberality to my visitors'.

Boerhaave had resolved to plant everything he could collect of trees, shrubs, bushes, his favourite family of *Umbelliferae*, and bulbs. The famous botanist Linnaeus often visited the park during his stay in the Netherlands; he called it 'a paradise, an incomparable arboretum'. According to Frans van Mieris, who wrote a description of the town of Leiden, the garden contained 'exotic trees and rare and foreign plants'. The so-called tulip tree, a tree originating from the East of North America, with yellow flowers which recall tulips, in 1837 was considered by an anonymous poet to be 'Nature's showpiece'.

Boerhaave gave much time to his country place. Here he found a refuge from his many demanding activities. 'When I am in despair because of all those tasks,' he wrote to Bassand, 'I walk out of the town and there I sow, plant, and I cultivate...'. In summer he went daily to and from his country estate, and at four o'clock on Friday he left Leiden to spend the weekend on Oud-Poelgeest. Then there were receptions on Sunday, with music. Boerhaave himself played the lute, and his daughter accompanied her songs on the harpsichord. On such occasions the Italian songs were also performed, which Bassand had sent for Johanna Maria. 'My daughter sings Italian Odes', thus Boerhaave in a letter of thanks, 'I admire their artistic charm, and so am able to relax.'

In 1737 the Italian musician Egidio Duni, 28 years old, consulted Boerhaave on Poelgeest. He was impressed both by Boerhaave's knowledge and by the youthful charm of his daughter. Duni gave an enraptured account of his stay there to his friend Carlo Goldoni. The latter used these data for a play, *Il medico Olandese*. In this play

104

the setting is Poelgeest, Boerhaave is renamed Bainer, 'Dutchman, physician, and philosopher'. Duni is replaced by a young Pole, who suffered from the same complaint as Duni, hypochondria. In the 'delightful garden' of Dr. Bainer's country place the Polish sufferer meets the physician's niece, 'Madame Marianne', and his heart cures his hypochondria, with the help of the common sense of Dr. Baines. A dowry of Hfl. 100.000,– is allotted to Marianne! The play's opening performance was in 1756, and it kept the stage until 1832. Evidently, Duni had concluded during his visit that Boerhaave was very well-to-do, and his daughter therefore a desirable match. However, Duni has not been given the opportunity with which Goldoni endowed his fictional counterpart.

After Boerhaave's death in 1738 his daughter Johanna Maria inherited Oud-Poelgeest. Her eldest daughter, Sybilla Maria de Thoms, succeeded her in 1791. In 1835 the manor was sold by public auction. One of its later owners, Mr. Gerrit Willink, in 1866 caused the two little turrets to be added to it, which considerably change its outline when viewed from the Mare. The municipality of Oegstgeest bought the manor with the surrounding grounds only in 1940. During and shortly after the war it housed soldiers; from 1946 on it is in use as an accommodation for conferences.

P.J.M.d.B./H.B.

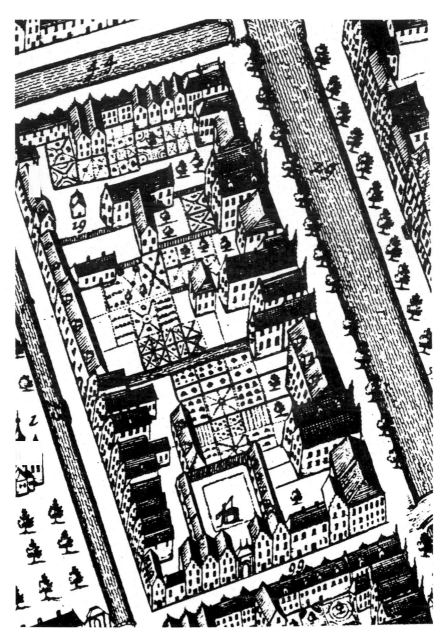

36.   Map of the Town of Leiden by C. Hagen (1670), detail.

106

The house no. 31 on the Rapenburg has a special place in the history of medicine in Leiden. A memorial tablet, put up in 1927, bears witness to the fact that Boerhaave died here on September 23, 1738. Yet he was not the first Professor of Medicine who lived in this house. It had been built in 1664 by the well-known 17th-century real estate agent Willem Wijmoth, at the expense of Boerhaave's illustrious predecessor, Franciscus de le Boë, Sylvius. His arms still embellish the gable in front.

In 1684, more than ten years after Sylvius's death, the house became the property of Jacob Trigland, Professor of Theology and Hebrew. The widow of his son sold it on March 27, 1730 to Susanna van de Blocquerie for the sum of Hfl. 15.000,–. Curiously, the latter sold it again on the same day, for the same price, to Boerhaave. In the purchase the wallpapers in the house were included, with the exception of the 'tapestries in the inner room'; the mirror and paintings in the mantelpiece of the inner room, the painting above the door of the inner room, the painting in the mantelpiece of the dining-room, and 'all the upright plates, even if they are moveable' (like hearth-plates), on the condition that an additional Hfl. 1000,– would be paid at the transfer. Apart from that, it was customary, when a house was bought, to donate a kind of gratuity to the neighbourhood in which it was situated; this was then spent by the local residents at a 'merry feast'. For this kind of capital houses such a gift could come up to Hfl. 25,– to 30,–; it is a pity that the bill of the neighbourhood Meyenburch has not been preserved, so that it cannot be discovered how much Boerhaave has paid.

Indubitably, it must have given Boerhaave a feeling of pride that he now possessed the house of a predecessor like Sylvius; for in the first years of his career he may well have looked up to the latter with some envy. Next door, moreover, on no. 29, lived the family of his colleague Bernhard Albinus, who had died in 1721, and who had been highly estimated by Boerhaave. Until 1736 Albinus's son Bernhard Siegfried lived with his mother in the house on the Rapenburg; he was a protégé of Boerhaave, and it has been partly due to Boerhaave's influence that in 1721 the young Albinus succeeded his father. Bernhard Siegfried Albinus, then, succeeded his father as Professor of Medicine, albeit in the Chair of Anatomy. Like his protector, he became a celebrity among the members of the Leiden University.

107

The immediate cause for buying Rapenburg 31, however, was rather serious. In the autumn of 1727 Boerhaave had been smitten by a fever which was so grave that people feared for his life. Boerhaave, by now 58 years old, had been so much weakened by the illness, that for some time he was unable to give his lectures. Perhaps it was in this period that the idea took hold of him to take things easier in the future. He therefore asked the Governors of the University to exempt him from the teaching of botany and chemistry; and in April 1729 Boerhaave resigned both professorships. A month earlier Adraan van Royen had been nominated lecturer of botany, but as yet he did not possess the 'great and special knowledge, long experience, and the continual correspondence with all famous Botanical Gardens of Universities and other well–stocked gardens' which was needed to enrich the *Hortus* with new plants. Hence the Governors asked Boerhaave 'for the time being to continue to live in the University's official residence giving on the Herb Garden' and to retain the 'general management of the Garden as well as the ensuing correspondence'. Evidently, Van Royen quickly learnt the ropes, for a year afterwards, on May 8, 1730, Boerhaave turned over the management of the *Hortus* to his successor.

During that year Boerhaave had ample opportunity to look for another house. It needs had to be a house containing a room for giving private lectures; for students received part of their tuition in the Professor's house – and paid extra for this! Moreover, the new house had to be equipped with a stable for Boerhaave's horse and gig. The large houses on the Rapenburg fully satisfied his requirements, but in this particular period few houses on the Rapenburg were for sale. Apart from a house on the Rapenburg close to the Doelensteeg, which was sold by public auction for Hfl. 22.000,–, only Rapenburg 31 was offered up for sale.

Its front may seem rather narrow, but because of its depth it is still a considerable property. It is one of the very rare houses of which the building specifications have been preserved; hence the original lay-out of 1664 can be almost exactly reconstructed. On the ground floor there was – apart from the long hallway, which extended from the front to the back of the house – a small room in front, giving a view of the Rapenburg, and the 'large drawing-room', looking out upon a little courtyard. In the courtyard stood the octagonal turret containing the staircase on which one could ascend to the upper storey. In the back part of the house were the kitchen, the dining-room, and a back room. Some of the remaining rooms had to do with Sylvius' profes-

37.     Rapenburg 31, Boerhaave's house. Photograph by J. Lens (1986).

sorships: for instance, the study, two laboratories, the room for distillation, and the lecture room.

Regrettably, we do not know whether the house had still the same layout in Boerhaave's time. It is certain, however, that his predecessor Trigland, already mentioned, had caused a little house in the backyard to be converted into a coach house. In any case, the house was sufficiently large to accommodate Boerhaave's professional activities. There must certainly have been a room for the private lectures: we know from subscription lists, dating from the last years of his professorship, that an average of rather more than hundred students put their names down for such lectures. Maybe there was also a laboratory, for Boerhaave continued to carry out chemical experiments up to six months before his death. There was also room for his collections. There were, for instance, three cabinets, painted green, with marine plants and 'little animals'; and, of course, his library. We do not know how Boerhaave's house was furnished. It has been said that he lived in a simple style; yet the rich interior stems already from the period of Boerhaave's daughter and even, possibly, of Boerhaave himself.

We have no more than incidental knowledge about other inhabitants of the house. In any case Herman's unmarried sister Jacoba Boerhaave lived with the family. Probably Boerhaave has also from 1733 to 1737 given house room to a student, his nephew Abraham Kaau, who was to become Professor of Medicine in St. Petersburg.

After Boerhaave's death his only daughter Johanna Maria inherited Rapenburg 31. Boerhaave's widow continued to live in with her daughter until her death in 1746; and when Johanna Maria's husband Frederik, Count de Thoms, died (in the same year 1746) she still continued to live there. It was only after her death in 1791 that her two daughters sold the house.                P.J.M.d.B.

110

38. Boerhaave's monument. Copperplate by A. Delfos. From: G. van Swieten's edition of Boerhaave's *Aphorisms*, (Vol. I, 1762).

Within the drawing:

SALVTIFERO
BOERHAVII
GENIO
SACRVM

39. Boerhaave's monument (front view). Wash drawing by J.H. Muntz (1772).

## 15. HEMSTERHUIS'S MONUMENT FOR BOERHAAVE

Many great figures of England's history have been laid at rest in Westminster Abbey. There their monumental tombs, often richly wrought, keep the memory of their important deeds green The Pieterskerk in Leiden has also some monuments of this kind, even if it is only a relatively small number, with the accent mainly on inhabitants of the town (1). The celebrities of the University are represented there by a few brilliant figures, and it was all but inevitable that a man like Herman Boerhaave is among them. It is a modest monument, in harmony with the spirit of simplicity which he advocated. A small vase of white marble, on a pedestal of black stone from Namur; on the latter one sees, again in white marble, a small portrait of Boerhaave – almost a miniature, one would say. Simplicity prevails everywhere, then; but the monument was designed by someone who knew what he wanted, and executed by gifted Dutch sculptors.

This monument has been made by order of Boerhaave's daughter, Johanna Maria. In 1741 she had married Frederik de Thoms, a rather adventurous character who had served at various European courts, and whose activities had been remunerated with a large fortune and the title of count. Moreover, during his stay in Italy he had amassed a large collection of Greek and Roman antiquities; among these was also a collection of carved stones.

The couple had two daughters. They lived in Boerhaave's house, Rapenburg 31, and also on Oud-Poelgeest. In both houses there was room for the antiquities. De Thoms died already in 1746; Tiberius Hemsterhuis, Professor of the Classical Languages, who lived in the house Rapenburg 47, and was a friend of the family Boerhaave, became one of the guardians of his young daughters. Now this Tiberius had a son, Frans, who applied himself to engineering. He was, moreover, a fanatical lover of classical Antiquity, a rather gifted draughtsman, and soon he also made a name as a philosopher. In 1755 he was appointed Clerk of the Council of State, an inconspicuous post which he filled conscientiously during many years. However, soon afterwards he was offered other work as well: an additional and unpaid job, which must have been far more to his taste, viz., the management of the collection of antiquities in the Cabinet of the Stadtholder in The Hague. In 1751 the mother of the young William V had bought for this Cabinet the collection of De Thoms in its

40a. The vase of white marble crowning Boerhaave's monument, before the restoration. Photograph by J. Lens (1986).

114

40b. The vase of white marble crowning Boerhaave's monument, after the restoration. Photograph by J. Lens (1986).

115

entirety from his heirs. Hemsterhuis naturally knew by his own observation this collection very well. He was an expert in this field, and so the right man on the right place in the new princely Cabinet. Hemsterhuis went to live in The Hague, and there, about 1760, the request of Boerhaave's daughter for him to design a monument for her father's grave must have reached him (2). Some years later he wrote his first important philosophical work, entitled *Lettre sur la sculpture* ... ; in this letter he tried to analyse the aesthetics of sculpture. Taking two vases, designed by him, as his starting-point, he put forward general criteria which ought to be met if beauty was to ensue. And the first of those two vases in its form resembles the design which he made for Boerhaave's monument.

Hemsterhuis had immersed himself in Antiquity to such an extent that he wholly identified with it. From his early youth onwards he had been introduced into the classical world. He had a real passion for collecting gems and cameos. Homer, Plato, and Sophocles were his favourite authors. Evidence for this can be found in his relationship with the Princess Gallitzin, the wife of the Russian ambassador. In this friendship, and following the lead of Plato's *Symposium*, Princess Gallitzin was given the name of Diotima, and Hemsterhuis that of Socrates. In their correspondence these names are regularly used. Indeed, Hemsterhuis regarded himself as a genuine Greek (3).

With that, it is characteristic of the period that the power of discernment with regard to the arts was still in its infancy. Hemsterhuis' collection of carved stones, which he, and almost everyone with him, viewed as items dating from classical Antiquity, actually consisted almost wholly of products of the Renaissance and later periods (4). This fitted in with the image of classical art, as yet imperfect, but generally prevailing; and it was characteristic for the fashion, mainly originating in Paris in the second half of the 18th century. This new trend was designated as 'le Goût Grec' or 'le Goût antique', and soon became widespread (5).

Hemsterhuis's design for Boerhaave's monument also fits into this trend. The memorial in the form of a vase was already characterised by a contemporary as being 'wholly in the antique taste'. It is a free remodelling of classical specimens; but the six little heads which are inserted around it constitute a motif unknown to Antiquity. They are linked together by a drapery; and with great care and a fine feeling for the composition of the whole Hemsterhuis has given them a prominent place in his design. They represent the four ages of man: infancy, youth, middle and old age, and so symbolise the gratitude of

41.    The monument after the restoration. Photograph by J. Lens (1986).

Boerhaave's patients for his work as a physician. The marble vase with its severe form and sober ornamentation is almost a sculptural counterpart of Boerhaave's motto: 'Simplicity is the hallmark of truth' (*simplex veri sigillum* ); but it gains its meaningful significance only through these six little heads. It is worth noting that in the first instance only representations of youths and men were envisaged; the small-scale model which was made prior to the actual sculpting, and which is still preserved in the Museum de Lakenhal, puts this beyond doubt (6). On second thoughts, however, it was evidently considered advisable that the grateful patients would be represented by women as well; hence Hemsterhuis included both sexes in his images of youth and old age.

For the realisation of the monument good sculptors from The Hague were enlisted: the stonemason Anthony Wapperon, who had the assistance of Ludovicus de Grave and Anthony Lannoy. It is owing to their craftsmanship that Hemsterhuis's concept was given the pure form which he so emphatically aimed at.

The monument dates from approximately 1760, and it is evident that Hemsterhuis must have followed the development of 'le Goût Grec' in Paris already in its earliest stage. He may have been brought in touch with it by the Count de Caylus, a prominent archaeologist and great champion of the new 'antique' style. Hemsterhuis corresponded with him and possessed a beautiful copy of De Caylus's *Recueil d'Antiquités* in seven volumes, the first of which was already published in 1752. Hemsterhuis may also have found inspiration in prints of French artists like, for instance, Jacques François Joseph Saly and the architect Jean-François de Neufforge (7).

The monument has been an ornament of the Pieterskerk for more than two centuries, and it did not survive undamaged. In particular the noses of most of the little heads, but also the brow of the man who symbolises old age, had been defaced during this long passage of time, through causes unknown. In 1986 the sculptor P. Reinhard, assisted by his wife, has restored it and removed the many layers of deeply ingrained dust from the marble. The monument, which is one of the oldest specimen of that style in our country, now seems, as it were, rejuvenated; it shines again, radiantly white, on its old place in the church, in honour of Herman Boerhaave and also, a little, of its designer Frans Hemsterhuis. Th.H.L.S.

118

LIST OF AUTHORS:

A.J.F.G.      A.J.F. Gogelein

A.M.L.-E.     A.M. Luyendijk-Elshout

D.F.K.        D.E. Krantz

H.B.          H. Beukers

J.Z.          J. Zuilhof

M.C.C.T.      M.C.C. Teune

P.J.M.d.B.    P.J.M. de Baar

R.R.          R. Ramakers

Th.H.L.S.     Th.H. Lunsingh Scheurleer

## PROVENANCE OF THE ILLUSTRATIONS:

Municipal Archive of Leiden: 8, 9, 11, 12, 13, 14, 21b, 27, 28, 30, 36, 39.

Research Institute of the National Herbarium and the Botanical Garden of the Leiden University: 24, 25, 26.

Museum Boerhaave, Leiden: 18, 20b.

Foundation 'The House of Boerhaave', Voorhout: 2, 3, 4, 5, 6, 7,

University Library of Leiden: 1, 10, 17, 19, 20a, 21a, 22, 23, 29, 34, 38.

Department Metamedica of the University of Leiden, section of the History of Medicine: 15, 16, 31, 32, 33, 35, 37, 40, 41.

# BIBLIOGRAPHY

## 1. GENERAL

### 1.1. On Herman Boerhaave:

G.A. Lindeboom, *Herman Boerhaave, the Man and his Work* (London, 1968).

G.A. Lindeboom, *Boerhaave's Correspondence* I (Leiden, 1962), II (Leiden, 1964), III (Leiden, 1979).

G.A. Lindeboom, *Boerhaave and his Time* (Leiden, 1970).

G.A. Lindeboom, *Haller in Holland. Het dagboek van Albrecht von Haller van zijn verblijf in Holland (1725-1727)* (Amsterdam, 1979).

*Herman Boerhaave, 1668-1738*. Catalogue of the exposition in the National Museum for the History of Science and Medicine, Leiden, 1968, Mededelingen nr. 136.

E. Ashworth Underwood, *Boerhaave's Men at Leyden and after* (Edinburgh, 1983).

E. Kegel-Brinkgreve, A.M. Luyendijk-Elshout, *Boerhaave's Orations. Translated with Introduction and Notes* (Leiden, 1983).

A. Schultens, *Academische redevoering ter gedachtenisse van den grooten Herman Boerhaave, ... uitgesproken op 4 november 1738*. With an Introduction by Dr. H.L. Houtzager (Amsterdam, 1988). In the series from the Foundation Historia Medicinae, nr. 2.

F.L.R. Sassen, 'Het geestelijk klimaat ten tijde van Herman Boerhaave', en J. Dankmeijer, 'Is Boerhaaves faam gerechtvaardigd?' in: *Herman Boerhaave, 1668/1968*. Leidse Voordrachten, 48 (Leiden, 1968).

E. Cohen, M. Renkema, *Herman Boerhaave en zijne Beteekenis voor de Chemie* (Utrecht, 1918).

E. Lesky, 'Albrecht von Haller, Gerard van Swieten und Boerhaave's Erbe', *Gesnerus* 15 (1958) 120-140.

### 1.2. On the University of Leiden:

P.C. Molhuysen, *Bronnen tot de geschiedenis der Leidsche Universiteit* ('s-Gravenhage, 1913-1914) 7 vols.

H.J. Witkam, *De dagelijkse zaken van de Leidse universiteit van 1581-1596* (Leiden, 1970-1974). 10 Vols. MS.

*Universiteit en Architectuur. Ontwerpen ten behoeve van de Leidse Universiteit 1600-1900.* Catalogue of the exposition on the occasion of the 25th anniversary of teaching the history of architecture at the University of Leiden, May 25 -June 23, 1979. With a Preface by J.J. Terwen.

H.A. van Oerle, 'Het Academiegebouw te Leiden', *Oudheidkundig Jaarboek* [= Bulletin K.N.O.B.] 6 (1937) 77-97.

Th.H. Lunsingh Scheurleer, G.H.M. Posthumus Meyes (eds.), *Leiden University in the Seventeenth Century. An Exchange of Learning* (Leiden, 1975).

*Leidse Universiteit 400. Stichting en eerste bloei 1575-ca. 1650.* Catalogue of the Exposition in the Rijksmuseum Amsterdam van March 27 - June 8, 1975.

G. Ruestow, *Physics at 17th and 18th Century Leiden, Philosophy and the new Science in the University* ('s Gravenhage, 1973).

**1.3. On the Town of Leiden:**

Th.H. Lunsingh Scheurleer, C.W. Fock, A.J. van Dissel, *Het Rapenburg. Geschiedenis van een Leidse gracht.* 6 Vols. (Leiden, 1986-1992).

J.Jz. Orlers, *Beschrijvinge van de stad Leyden* (Leiden, 1614; 2d enlarged ed., 1641).

[J.N. de Parival], *Les Délices de Leide, etc.* (Leiden, 1712).

F. van Mieris, *Beschrijving der stad Leyden [etc.]* Continued by D. van Alphen (Leiden, 1762-1784). 3 Vols.

A. Rademaker, *Rhynlands Fraaiste Gezichten* (Amsterdam, 1732). Reprint Kruseman ('s Gravenhage, 1967).

2. *SPECIAL SUBJECTS*

**2.2. The Boerhaave house in Voorhout:**

J. Kok, *Bijvoegzels op het Vaderlandsch Woordenboek* I, A-B (Amsteldam, 1797), 226-242.

J. van Dobbelen, 'Boerhaavehuis en Hervormde Kerk te Voorhout', *Geïllustreerd Weekblad Buiten,* June 9, 1917.

W. de Mooij, *Uit Voorhouts Verleden* (Arnhem, 1964).

A.M. Hulkenberg, *De Bartholomeüskerk van Voorhout* (Alphen a.d. Rijn, 1983).

J.T.P. Bijhouwer, *Nederlandsche Tuinen en Buitenplaatsen* (Amsterdam, 1942).

*The Anglo-Dutch Garden in the Age of William & Mary,* English and Dutch, ed. J. Dixon Hunt, special double issue of *Journal of Garden History* (1988), London.

H. Johnson, *The International Book of Trees* (London, 1973).

C.S. Oldenburger-Ebbers, *De Tuinengids van Nederland* (Rotterdam, 1989).


**2.3. The Latin school:**

W.H.D. Suringar, 'Bouwstoffen voor eene oordeelkundige beschouwing van den aard en toestand van het Gymnasiaal Onderwijs hier te lande in de twee vorige eeuwen; en tevens voor een geschiedenis van de Laijnsche School te Leyden in diezelfde tijden'. Offprint from: *Tijdchrift voor de Nederlandsche gymnasia voor 1863-1864.*

J.F.Dröge, 'De Latijnse School en de Rectorswoning', *Leids Jaarboekje* 78 (1986) 35-52.

A.M. Coebergh van de Braak, *Meer dan zes eeuwen Leids gymnasium* (Leiden, 1988).

L. Knappert, 'Uit de geschiedenis der Latijnsche school te Leiden', *Leids Jaarboekje* 1 (1904) 93-139 en 2 (1905) 14-48.

Rijksmuseum Boerhaave te Leiden, Archief, 217. Letters exchanged between the Municipal Archive and the Museum.

Municipal Archive Leiden, Notarieel Archief inv.nr 1196, J. van der Stoffe, akte 127. Municipal Archive Leiden, Stadsarchief 1594-1816 inv.nr 3349 en 3341.


**2.5. Living in the Begijnhof:**

F.W.J. Koorn, *Begijnhoven in Holland en Zeeland gedurende de Middeleeuwen* (Assen, 1981).

H.J. de Jonge, 'Peregrinatio Heinsiana. Onderzoek naar de plaatsen waar Daniel Heinsius te Leiden gewoond heeft en naar de plaats van zijn graf', *Leids Jaarboekje* 65 (1973) 51-67.


**2.6. The *Theatrum Anatomicum* or Dissecting Room:**

H.J. Witkam, *Over de anatomieplaats, de Albinussen en de Sandiforts* (Leiden, 1968) 6-28. MS.

J.A.J. Barge, *De oudste inventaris der oudste academische anatomie in Nederland* (Leiden, 1934).

A.J.F. Gogelein, 'Het Theatrum Anatomicum als gebouw' in: *Leidse Universiteit 400. Stichting en eerste Bloei 1575-ca 1650.* Catalogue of the exposition in the Rijksmuseum Amsterdam van 27 maart-8 juni 1975, 100-103.

Th.H. Lunsingh Scheurleer, 'Un Amphithéâtre d'Anatomie moralisée' in: Th.H. Lunsingh Scheurleer, G.H.M. Posthumus Meyes (eds.) *Leiden University in the Seventeenth Century. An Exchange of Learning* (Leiden, 1975) 216-277.

A.M. Luyendijk-Elshout, 'Antony Nuck (1650-1692). The Mercator of the Body Fluids' in: *Circa Tiliam. Studia Historiae Medicinae Gerrit Arie Lindeboom septuagenario oblata* (Leiden, 1974) 150-164.

## 2.7. The Library:

H.J. Witkam, *Iets over Pieter Paaw en zijn Theatrum Anatomicum, en over het bouwen van de Anatomieplaats en de Bibliotheek* (Leiden, 1967) 18-28 MS.

P.C. Molhuysen, *Geschiedenis der Universiteitsbibliotheek te Leiden* (Leiden, 1905).

H.W. Tydeman, 'Authentieke geschiedenis van den aankoop van de bibliotheek van Is. Vossius voor de Akademie te Leiden' *Mnemosyne, Mengelingen voor wetenschap en Fraaije Letteren* 5 (1825) 260-290.

F.F. Blok, *Contributions to the history of Isaac Vossius' library,* Verhandelingen der Koninklijke Nederlandse Akademie van Wetenschappen, Afdeling Letterkunde, Nieuwe Reeks, 83 (Amsterdam, 1974).

## 2.8. Professor at the University:

M. Ultee, 'The Politics of Professorial Appointment at Leiden, 1709', *History of Universities* 9 (1990) 167-193.

W.P. Jorissen, *Het chemisch (thans anorganisch chemisch) Laboratorium der Universiteit te Leiden van 1859-1909 en de chemische laboratoria voor dat tijdvak en zij die erin doceerden* (Leiden, 1909).

## 2.9. The Botanical Garden:

L.G.M. Baas Becking, H. Veendorp, *The Development of the Gardens of Leyden University* (Haarlem, 1938) 99-127.

W.K.H. Karstens, H. Kleibrink, *De Leidse Hortus. Een botanische Erfenis.* (Zwolle, 1982).

H. Boerhaave, *Index Plantarum quae in horto academico Lugduno Batavo reperiuntur* (Leiden, 1710) en: *Index Alter Plantarum quae in horto academico Lugduno Batavo aluntur* (Leiden, 1720). Pars I and II. With a map.

126

J.H. Heniger, 'Some Botanical Activities of Herman Boerhaave, Professor of Botany and Director of the Botanic garden at Leyden', *Janus. Revue Internationale de l'Histoire des Sciences de la Médicine, de la Pharmacie et de la Technique* 58 (1971) 1-78.

F.W.T. Hunger, 'Boerhaave als natuurhistoricus', *Nederlands tijdschrift voor Geneeskunde* 63 1A (1919) 36-44.

G.A. Lindeboom, 'Boerhaave in Harderwijk', *Bijdragen en Mededelingen der Vereniging 'Gelre'* 63 (1968) 103-117.

G.A. Uittien, 'Boerhaave's beteekenis voor de plantkunde', *Nederlands Tijdschrift voor Geneeskunde* 82 (1938) 4841-4851.

C. Linnaeus, *Species Plantarum.* Tomus I (Stockholm, 1753) 145.


**2.11. The Caecilia Hospital and Clinical Teaching:**

H. Beukers, 'Clinical teaching in Leiden from its beginning until the end of the eighteenth century', *Clio Medica* 21 (1987/88) 139-152.

J. Denijs, Verhandelingen over het ampt des vroedmeesters en vroedvrouwen (1733) 162.

G.A. Lindeboom, *Boerhaave's Correspondence*, Vol. II, 252.

E.C. van Leersum, 'Boerhaaves dictaten, inzonderheid zijner klinische lessen', *Nederlandsch Tijdschrift voor Geneeskunde* 63 (1919) 50-76.

J.A.J. Barge, *De stichting van het academisch klinisch onderwijs te Leiden voor 300 jaren* (Leiden, 1937).

J.A.J. Barge, 'Het Collegium medico-practicum in het voormalige Caecilia-Gasthuis', *Leids Jaarboekje* 29 (1936/1937) 49-58.

J.A.J. Barge, 'Het geneeskundig onderwijs aan de Leidsche Universiteit in de 18e eeuw', *Nederlands Tijdschrift voor Geneeskunde* 78 (1934) 47-68.

H.A. van Oerle, 'De Bouw van het St. Caecilia Gasthuis in de Camp te Leiden', *Leids Jaarboekje* 33 (1941) 63-81.

M.W. Jongsma, *325 jaar Academisch Ziekenhuis te Leiden* (Lochem, 1963).

A.M. Luyendijk-Elshout, 'The Caecilia Hospital in Leiden (1600-1972)' in: *Proc. XXIII Int. Congress of the Hist. of Med. London 2-9 Sept. 1972.* I (1974) 312-317.


**2.12. The Weighhouse and the Surgeons' Chamber:**

H.J. Jesse, 'De Waag te Leiden', *Leids Jaarboekje* 6 (1909) 135-141.

127

G.J. Boekenoogen, 'Namen en wapens van Leidsche Chirurgijns', *Leids Jaarboekje* 21 (1927/28) 78-101.

Ch. Tiels, A.M. Luyendijk-Elshout, 'De Leidse chirurgijns en hun kamer boven de Waag', *Nederlands Kunsthistorisch Tijdschrift* 31 (1980) 215-238.

## 2.13. Oud-Poelgeest:

W.J.J.C. Bijleveld, 'Een en ander uit de geschiedenis van het kasteel Oud-Poelgeest', *Leids Jaarboekje* 1 (1904) 140-149.

W.J.J.C. Bijleveld, 'Oud-Poelgeest', *Leids Jaarboekje* 4 (1907) 75-92.

I.W.L. Moerman, R. Brandenburg, *Het kasteel Oud-Poelgeest*, serie Nederlandse kastelen VIII (1977).

*De Hollandse Dokter*. Comedy of Carlo Goldoni. Translated from the Italian by J.A. Verhaart-Bodderij (Delft, 1968).

## 2.14. Rapenburg 31:

L. Knappert, [Bladvulling] *Leids Jaarboekje* 28 (1935/36) 31-32.

Th.H. Lunsingh Scheurleer, C.W. Fock, A.J. van Dissel, *Het Rapenburg. Geschiedenis van een Leidse gracht* Vol. III (Leiden, 1988) 270-354.

H. Beukers, 'Het Laboratorium van Sylvius', *Tijdschrift voor de Geschiedenis der Geneeskunde, Natuurwetenschappen en Techniek* 3 (1980) 28-36.

## 2.15. Hemsterhuis's monument for Boerhaave:

(1)   K.J.F.C. Kneppelhout van Sterkenburg, *De gedenkteekenen in de Pieterskerk te Leyden* (Leiden, 1864).

(2)   This may be deduced from the Journal of the Churchwardens in Leiden (Municipal Archive of Leiden) d.d. September 6, 1762. On that date Johanna Maria de Thoms-Boerhaave donated the sum of ƒ 1.000,- to the churches 'because of a certain monument being put up to commemorate ... Hermanus Boerhaave...'.

(3)   L. Brummel, *Frans Hemsterhuis. Een philosofenleven* (Haarlem, 1925).
E. Taverne, *Frans Hemsterhuis als verzamelaar, tekenaar en archeoloog*. Catalogue of the exposition of the Hemsterhuis-symposium, Slot Oud-Zuilen, 1969.

(4)   A.N. Zadoks-Josephus Jitta, *Hemsterhuis als gemmenverzamelaar*. Symposium on Frans Hemsterhuis, 75-78.

128

(5)   Svend Eriksen, *Early Neo-Classicism in France* (London, 1974).

(6)   E. Pelinck, *Catalogue of the Stedelijk Museum 'De Lakenhal', Beeldhouw-werken*.. (Leiden, 1951) nr. 25, 9h.

(7)   Eriksen, *op. cit.* p. 375, figs. 291, 379 and figs. 310-318.

# CONTENTS

# LIST OF LOCATIONS

1. The Boerhaave house in Voorhout.
2. The Latin school in the Lokhorststraat.
3. The University Building on the Rapenburg.
4. The Begijnhof on the Rapenburg.
5. Rear view of the Faliede Begijnkerk, former domicile of the Anatomical Theatre.
6. The University Garden
7. The Caecilia Hospital, now Museum Boerhaave.
8. The Weighhouse, formerly the domicile of the Guild of Surgeons.
9. The manor Oud-Poelgeest.
10. House of Boerhaave, Rapenburg 31.
11. Boerhaave's monument in the Pieterskerk.